The Puzzle Master

Other Publications:
TIME-LIFE LIBRARY OF CURIOUS AND UNUSUAL FACTS
AMERICAN COUNTRY
VOYAGE THROUGH THE UNIVERSE
THE THIRD REICH
THE TIME-LIFE GARDENER'S GUIDE
MYSTERIES OF THE UNKNOWN
TIME FRAME
FIX IT YOURSELF
FITNESS, HEALTH & NUTRITION
SUCCESSFUL PARENTING
HEALTHY HOME COOKING
LIBRARY OF NATIONS
THE ENCHANTED WORLD
THE KODAK LIBRARY OF CREATIVE PHOTOGRAPHY
GREAT MEALS IN MINUTES
THE CIVIL WAR
PLANET EARTH
COLLECTOR'S LIBRARY OF THE CIVIL WAR
THE EPIC OF FLIGHT
THE GOOD COOK
WORLD WAR II
HOME REPAIR AND IMPROVEMENT
THE OLD WEST

This volume is one of a series that examines
various aspects of computer technology
and the role computers play in modern life.

UNDERSTANDING COMPUTERS

The Puzzle Master

BY THE EDITORS OF TIME-LIFE BOOKS
TIME-LIFE BOOKS, ALEXANDRIA, VIRGINIA

Contents

6   ESSAY   Painting Nature by the Numbers
     Seeing Patterns and Connections
     ESSAY   Computer Sleuths in the Museum

51   The Language Machine
     ESSAY   Networks of Knowledge

93   Peepholes to the Future
     ESSAY   Understanding the Unpredictable

122   Bibliography
124   Picture Credits
125   Acknowledgments
126   Index

1

2

3

Painting Nature by the Numbers

The modern tools of scientific inquiry provide an almost overwhelming amount of information on a wide range of subjects. Sophisticated instruments detect and measure eve-

rything from ozone in the Earth's atmosphere to the magnetic field of Uranus, filling computer memories with countless billions of bits of data. The computer, which is so essential in the collecting, storing, and analyzing of that information, also plays a significant role in making the information easier to comprehend. As demonstrated here and on the following pages, computers are frequently used to express facts and figures visually, translating huge masses of data into portraits that can be read at a glance.

The highly detailed image of oceanic wind patterns below

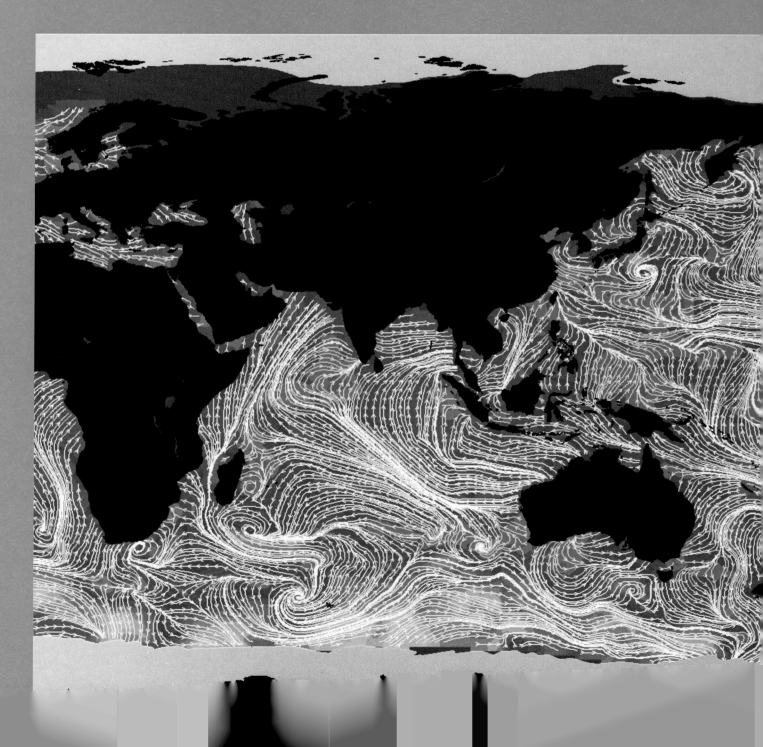

began with raw data from NASA's *SEASAT*, an orbiting satellite that bounced radar beams off the ocean surface and then measured how tiny wavelets driven by surface winds scattered the reflected beams. A computer program processed these measurements through complex formulas to determine both wind speed and direction. The millions of numbers that resulted meant little until graphics software turned them into lines and colors, allowing oceanographers and meteorologists to see patterns that might otherwise have remained buried in digital obscurity.

Mapping ocean winds. This computer-generated image of ocean wind patterns is based on more than 150,000 surface-wind measurements made by satellite-borne radar during a single day. White lines with arrows indicate the direction of wind flow, and colors denote wind speed, with blue for the lowest speeds and yellow for the highest. Swirling patterns that curve counter-clockwise in the Northern Hemisphere and clockwise in the Southern Hemisphere identify storm systems.

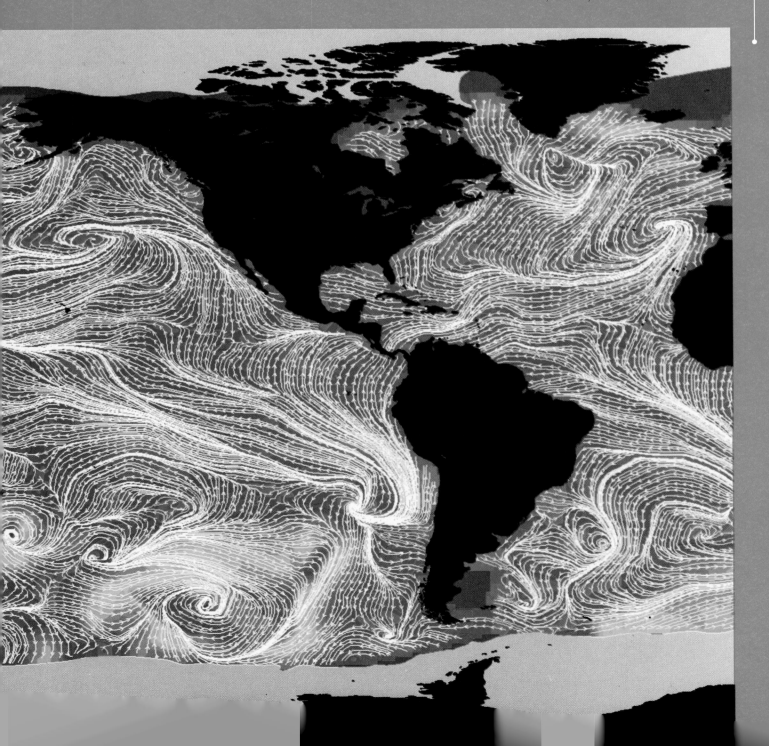

Uncovering a Hole in the Ozone

Depletion of atmospheric ozone, believed to be caused by the release of chemical compounds known as chlorofluorocarbons, represents a potentially serious threat to life on Earth. Without an ozone shield, plants and animals—including humans—would be exposed to dangerously high levels of ultraviolet radiation from the Sun. In the 1970s, scientists began collecting data on ozone levels worldwide from the ground, air, and space. Some observations indicated that the ozone level was unusually low during the spring in the South Polar region, and satellite readings confirmed the findings. But the problem did not really go public until the mid-1980s, when computer-imaging techniques brought the evidence before the world's eyes.

The data for images came from a satellite equipped with a sensing instrument called a spectrometer, specially attuned to detect the wavelengths of sunlight that pass through ozone in the upper atmosphere as they reflect off dust particles, clouds, and the Earth's surface. The spectrometer rated the brightness of the reflected light on a scale ranging from 0 to 255, taking almost 200,000 separate measurements daily around the globe. Ground-based computers then used the brightness values to calculate the amount of ozone at each location where measurements were taken. By plugging these figures into graphics-generating software, scientists were able to create several different visual versions of the data to aid in the task of analyzing this complex phenomenon.

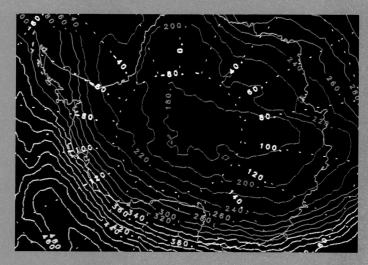

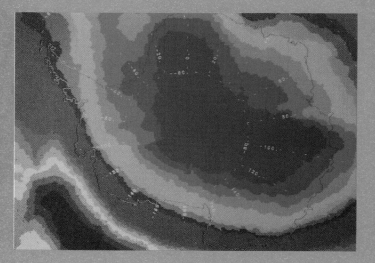

Two methods of mapping. Shown on this page are two basic visualization techniques for representing the thickness of the ozone layer over Antarctica, outlined above in pink and at right in blue. The contour lines above delineate differing levels in Dobson units, where one unit is equivalent to a layer of ozone one-thousandth of a centimeter thick; yellow lines denote above-average levels, red lines average, and blue lines lower than average. The image at right uses additional colors and shades to emphasize the variations, this time with red signifying the highest levels.

A three-dimensional view. By translating ▶ ozone measurements into both color and height, the image at right clearly demonstrates the concept of a hole in the ozone above the South Pole. High ozone levels appear as red and yellow peaks, which drop off in green and then light blue slopes to the dark blue depression in the center that represents the thinnest region of ozone. Sophisticated graphics software is necessary to create the proper shading that gives the image a three-dimensional appearance.

Charting the Course of a Deadly Storm

In many regions of the world, rainy and dry seasons occur with such clockwork regularity that science can add little to traditional knowledge of when and where rain will fall. But occasionally along the west coast of South America, changes in ocean currents and trade winds—known as El Niño events because they tend to arrive near Christmas—create havoc with local climates: Storms dump immense quantities of rain on areas unaccustomed to more than a few inches per year, bursting dams, washing away houses, and causing great loss

A rainstorm's progress. The sequence of computer-generated images at right illustrates the pattern of rainfall in northwestern Peru during a three-day period in January 1983. A three-dimensional grid portrays the local topography, with altitude in meters; the Pacific coast is outlined in pink below the grid. A color scale *(near right)* represents the daily rainfall in millimeters, ranging from 0 *(blue)* to 200 *(red)*. On the first day *(top)*, heavy rain falls inland as the storm breaks against the Andean foothills. Cold air sweeping down from the high Andes intensifies the precipitation on the second day *(middle)*. By the third day *(bottom)*, the storm has slackened somewhat but will regain its strength as it continues to interact with the mountains.

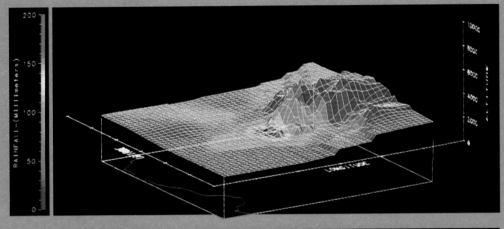

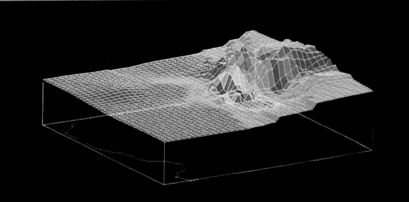

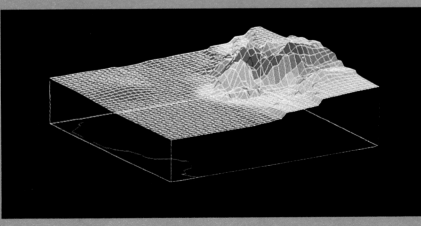

of life. Computer visualizations have proved useful in helping meteorologists understand the unusual weather patterns that characterize these events.

The study illustrated on these pages made use of data gathered from sixty-six weather stations scattered throughout northwestern Peru. A computer compiled rainfall measurements from each of the stations and, in order to create a continuous pattern of rainfall over the region, extrapolated measurements for the areas lying between stations. All this information was then displayed graphically on a computer simulation of the landscape.

A sequence of images for several consecutive days reveals the initial eastward course of a storm and its recoil off the mountains and back to the customarily dry plains that lie along the seacoast. Such animated views clearly demonstrate the significant effect that local topography can have on the development and direction of a storm and where it will unleash its greatest fury.

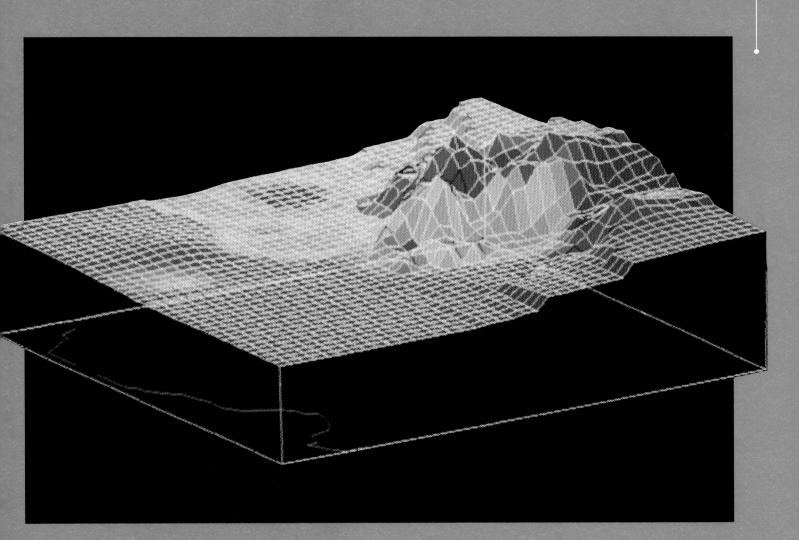

The final deluge. By day four, the heart of the storm system has shifted to the northwest, in effect having rebounded off the mountains and back toward the coast with renewed vigor. The intense rainfall denoted by the red patch occurred over a very short time and caused devastating floods and mud slides on the normally arid coastal plain.

Computerized Views of the Clouds

Any study of the Earth's climate must take into account the crucial role played by clouds. Besides delivering life-giving rain to the land, clouds help maintain a proper balance in the global climate: As the Sun heats bodies of water and land-masses, clouds build up and block some of the solar radiation, allowing the surface to cool; when the clouds subside, the Sun gets through again and the process begins anew. The varied features of the Earth's surface, as well as the prevailing patterns of the wind, greatly influence the formation and distribution of clouds. Computer graphics that allow scientists to visualize these effects have provided important insights into the dynamics of global weather systems.

Creating three-dimensional views of cloud patterns is much easier said than done. Data for the images shown here, for example, was gathered by a weather satellite armed with twenty-two different sensors taking a wide range of measurements of the atmosphere. Complex algorithms containing as many as one and a half million lines of computer coding derived both the height and the thickness of clouds from these measurements.

Daily readings over the course of a month were then compiled and the results displayed as a three-dimensional model of the global cloud cover that could be viewed from all sorts of angles, revealing in sharp detail how clouds tend to dissipate over landmasses such as Australia and build up where trade winds converge.

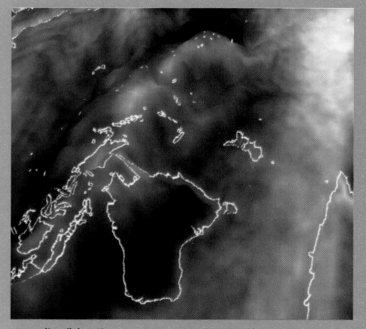
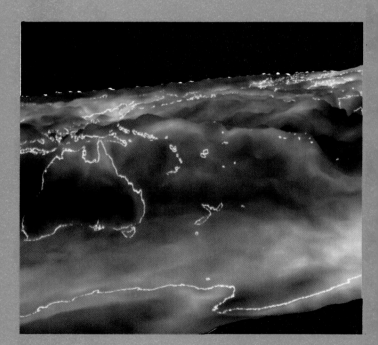

Australian flyby. The computer-generated images above and opposite illustrate the topography of the cloud cover over Australia and the southern Pacific for the month of January 1979. Cloud opacity is denoted by color, with white representing the thickest clouds and blue representing little or no cloud cover. The three-dimensional model can be manipulated to change the perspective, as if the observer were actually flying over the simulated cloud landscape. As the point of view moves from west to east in the two images above, variations in cloud height—from low, thick clouds near Antarctica *(right, bottom)* to ridges of high cloud farther north—become more apparent.

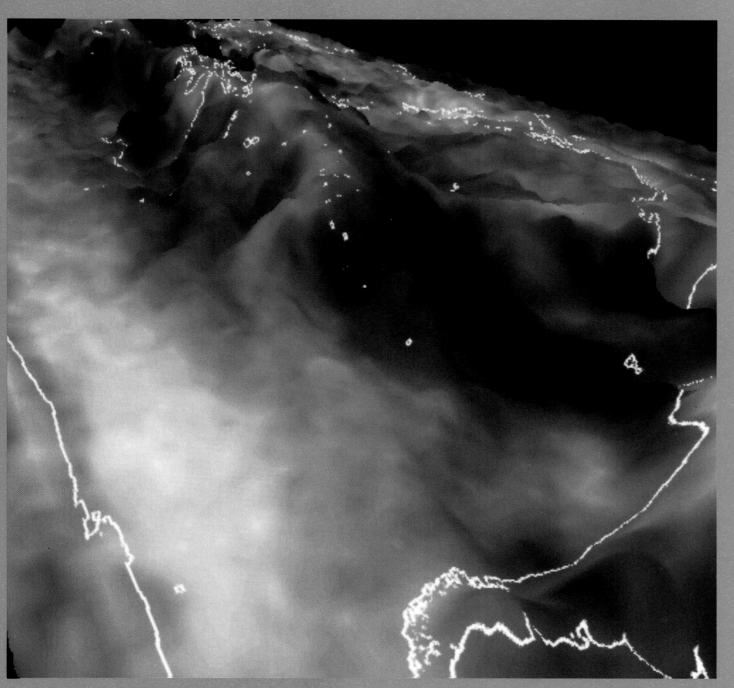

A mountainous ribbon of clouds. A view of the same cloud topography from far to the east emphasizes the long ridge of high clouds stretching from Australia *(top)* to South America *(bottom)*. This band represents an important global weather system where trade winds converge, forcing up moist air and thus giving rise to heavy rainfall in the tropics during the Southern Hemisphere's spring and summer.

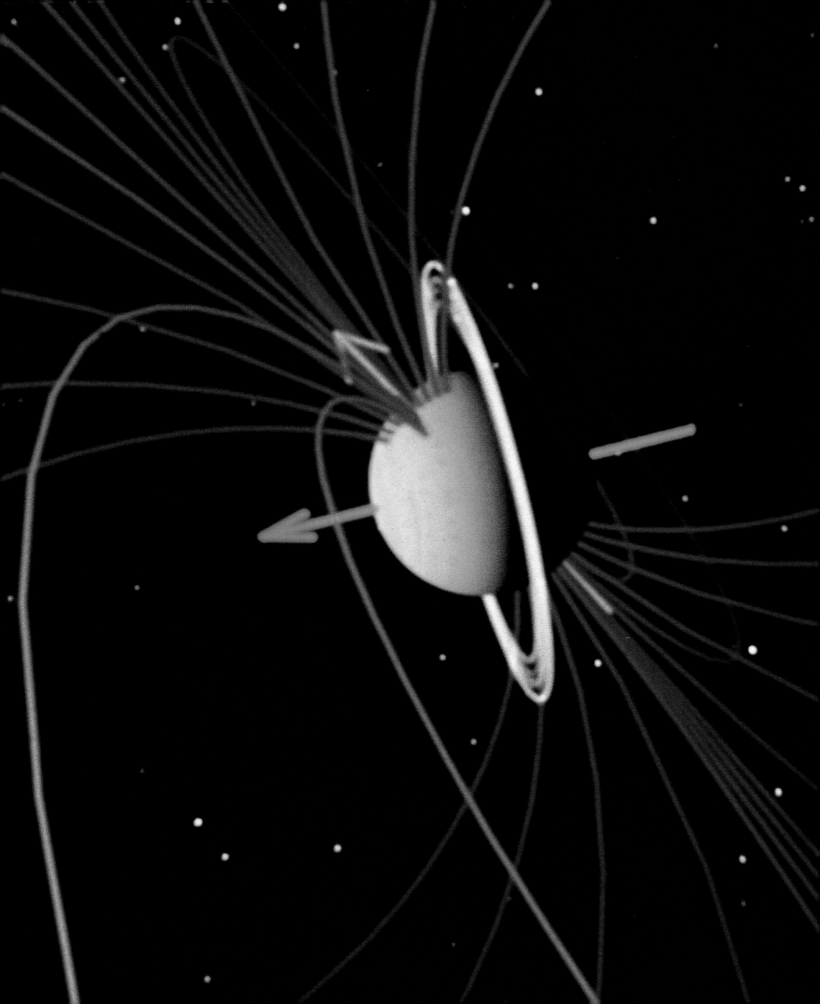

Magnetic Mysteries of a Distant Planet

When the deep-space probe *Voyager 2* first encountered Uranus in January 1986, its instruments discovered a surprising phenomenon: The axis of the planet's dipolar magnetic field, unlike those of other planets such as Earth, was tilted from its axis of rotation by about sixty degrees. Typically, as a planet rotates, electrically conducting material in its liquid core induces a magnetic field whose axis tends to align with the rotational axis, sending lines of magnetic force far out into space to form a so-called magnetosphere around the planet. Uranus was already noteworthy for the unusual characteristic of lying on its side as it circles the Sun; *Voyager's* findings about the orientation of Uranus's magnetosphere were a further puzzle.

Although scientists are hard-pressed to explain the causes of Uranus's strange magnetic dynamics, computer visualization of *Voyager's* data has at least provided a clear picture of what those dynamics are. Magnetometers aboard the satellite took thousands of measurements of magnetic forces near Uranus, detecting the interactions of the Uranian magnetic field with that of the Sun. Transmitted nearly two billion miles back to Earth, the data was used to derive a complex mathematical model of the planet's magnetosphere, and computer graphics depicted the results. By studying how the lines of magnetic force in the computer animation varied over time *(right)*, scientists were able to analyze in detail the effects of the planet's oddly out-of-kilter system.

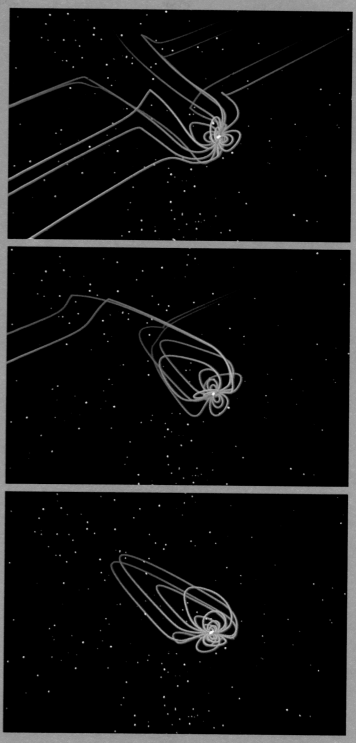

◄ **A skewed magnetic field.** This computer simulation illustrates the unique orientations of Uranus and its magnetic field—the rotational axis *(aqua arrow)* pointing sunward and the magnetic axis *(purple arrow)* pitched almost perpendicular to it. Lines of magnetic force extend into space from one end of the magnetic axis and return at the other.

Rhythmic variation. Frames from an animated sequence show how Uranus's magnetosphere varies in shape as the planet rotates. At top, magnetic lines extend outward to connect with the Sun's magnetic field. As the Uranian magnetosphere shifts alignment after four *(middle)* and then eight *(bottom)* hours, fewer lines interact with the solar magnetic field.

Seeing Patterns and Connections

At ten o'clock on the moonlit night of October 11, 1492, Admiral Christopher Columbus spotted a faint glimmer far ahead, a "dim thing" that rose into view with the ship's motion and then disappeared beyond the white-capped swells. By two o'clock the next morning, Columbus had sailed close enough to confirm the vision: For the ninety men and boys aboard the three ships in his flotilla, it was the first sight of land in thirty-three days at sea. But what land was it?

Columbus believed he was nearing Cipango, or modern-day Japan. Upon going ashore, he and his landing party met a group of Indians who identified the place as the island of Guanahani. Columbus called it San Salvador, after the Savior. But in the years since then, the precise site of the landfall—generally acknowledged to be somewhere in the central Bahamas—has become one of the most perplexing puzzles that geographers and historians have ever tackled.

The mystery arises from the difficulty of interpreting Columbus's log of the voyage. The original is lost; all that survives is a paraphrase made by the priest and historian, Bartolomé de las Casas. So many are its ambiguities and its suspected errors and omissions that scholars attempting to decipher the log have proposed ten different Bahamian islands as the spot where Columbus first set foot in the New World. The puzzle seemed solved in 1942, when Columbus biographer Samuel Eliot Morison declared one of the ten candidates, Watling Island, to be the actual site. "There is no longer any doubt," Morison proclaimed after years of study and analysis. "I consider the question settled once for all." However, Morison's faith in his conclusion proved to have been misplaced.

In 1986, a small team of humanists and scientists used a powerful mainframe computer—a Control Data Corporation Cyber 170/865—to come up with a likelier resolution to the debate. The group developed an interactive computer system, called the Columbus Research Tool (CRT), that they believe has allowed them to re-create electronically the epic course through the Bahamas that Columbus had followed five centuries earlier. The CRT features, among other things, a software algorithm that computes the maximum distance at which a given island would first have been visible from the crow's nest of his flagship, the *Santa Maria*. Through the combined action of such high-tech helpmates, the CRT's developers hoped to settle, once and for all, the identity of the dim thing on the horizon that October night.

A KNACK FOR PUZZLES

Like the men and women who conceived the Columbus Research Tool, scholars and scientists in almost every field of human endeavor are using computers to unlock puzzles that have long defied solution. A combination of two basic traits has made the computer an ideal instrument for solving puzzles: It can classify and tabulate enormous quantities of information, and it can quickly process that information to generate possible answers to a multitude of questions.

In both the social and the physical sciences, enigmas that have stymied the greatest minds since the time of Archimedes—a Greek mathematician fond of creating brain-bogglers for his rivals—have begun yielding up their secrets to computerized inquiry. Computers have been put to work as literary detectives, for example, unearthing clues about everything from the composition date of Ernest Hemingway's *The Old Man and the Sea* to the authorship of works attributed to William Shakespeare and Russian novelist Mikhail Sholokhov. Computers have also been employed in a bid to master the most difficult puzzle of all, the future: Using elaborate mathematical constructs known as computer models, an eclectic band of meteorologists, economists, and physicists are striving to forecast tomorrow's weather, next year's national economy, and even the earth's environment into the twenty-first century.

The computer's unique ability to detect patterns and relationships in large bodies of knowledge has proved to be of special benefit in the data-rich disciplines of history and archaeology, as well as in the seemingly unrelated but nonetheless computationally intensive field of mathematics. Computerized historical studies, for example, have shaken accepted tenets about the mechanics of tyranny in the antebellum South, while computers themselves have been put to use as tools for teaching history. In archaeology, digital machines have brought remarkable advances in the speed and precision of data collection, and their deftness at ferreting out patterns in that data has permitted a more thorough scrutiny than ever before of the clues combed from a site. The computer's powers of recognition have enabled mathematicians, too, to follow new angles of attack toward classic puzzles. These include the traveling-salesman problem—a notorious route-finding exercise that has begun to yield to the computer's facility at finding the best connections among points on a map—as well as the computation of pi, a value having an apparently endless string of digits that may disclose some significant pattern to computer analysis.

COURTING CLIO BY COMPUTER

The decade of the 1950s, wrote history professor Edward Shorter in 1971, was an era when many historians thought of the computer as "somebody who kept score at baseball games." By midpoint in the decade, however, several forward-thinking students of the past had begun to experiment with punch cards and sorting machines as tools for a new science called cliometrics—the study of history, domain of the muse Clio, by means of statistical analysis and mathematical techniques. A small but visionary group, the cliometricians of the 1950s sought to uncover significant patterns in such data as colonial shipping records, nineteenth-century census takings, and the biographies and voting records of legislators in the United States and Britain.

The wealth of statistical detail preserved in these and other documents made the computer, when it first began to appear on college campuses in the late 1950s, an ideal tool for exploring history. In the computer, remarked Pomona College history professor Robert Woods, Jr., historians found "an aide with uncomplaining precision, obedience, and singular devotion to

relieving the tedium of repetition and the expense of large-scale analysis."

Among the first American scholars to employ digital methods of historical inquiry was Merle Curti. A professor of history at the University of Wisconsin and a pioneer in cliometrics, Curti set out to test the validity of a famous thesis put forward in 1893 by another University of Wisconsin professor, Frederick Jackson Turner. Turner's "frontier thesis" suggested that the unique character of American democracy was the product of the American frontier with its free land, its economic opportunity, and above all, its economic equality.

In 1951, drawing on original documents from the U.S. Censuses of 1860, 1870, and 1880, Curti, his wife, and several assistants transcribed to some 17,000 IBM punch cards personal information on nearly 10,000 frontiersmen and their families living in Trempealeau County, Wisconsin. Details included age, birthplace, occupation, family size, household income, and personal property. Curti fed the cards— called unit records—through some rudimentary data-processing machinery known as unit-record equipment. This apparatus was used in the 1950s to perform the repetitive reading of punch cards necessary to sort, calculate, and summarize the data.

The patterns that emerged from this herculean processing task indicated that the community had indeed witnessed an economic equalization over time. The income of the poor grew faster than that of the rich, persuading Curti that Turner's thesis was sound. Curti's methods and results, wrote historian Allan Bogue in 1968, "gave respectability to quantification," sowing the seeds for future projects that aimed to computerize the past.

THE GRANDDADDY OF DATA BANKS

The toddling science of cliometrics got a steadying hand in 1962 when a group of political scientists at the University of Michigan founded the Interuniversity Consortium for Political and Social Research (ICPSR). Among the ICPSR's early steps was the creation, with the cooperation of quantitative historians, of a mammoth data bank called the Historical Archive. Located in Ann Arbor, Michigan, the archive would grow to be of vital importance to a generation of historians using computers.

Researchers began filling this data vault with statistics in 1965. By the early 1970s, it had swallowed up more than 880 megabytes (880 million characters) of historical fact: results of every U.S. Census since 1790; congressional roll-call votes from the days of the Continental Congress; and county-level election returns for members of congress, state governors, and U.S. presidents from 1824 on. The electoral data alone represented 20,000 contests involving more than 100,000 candidates for office. Scholars responded avidly to this cornucopia: Between 1969 and 1974, the collection supplied historians and social scientists with three billion characters of answers.

The archive's information is available only in computer-readable form. Answers to queries are provided primarily on magnetic tape, although remote access to the collection is possible via telephone and modem. Microcomputer users can obtain data on floppy disks. As Shorter predicted in 1971, such ready access to so much information has caused historians tilling other corners of the field to "regard their colleagues in American history with some envy."

The envy stems from the archive's ability to answer questions once deemed unanswerable. Beginning in 1850, for example, U.S. Census figures provide detailed information about the age, occupation, birthplace, parents' birthplace, personal-property value, and literacy of all the nation's citizens. Subjected to computer analysis, these statistics can reveal patterns of social structure and change that might escape unautomated scrutiny. The archive has helped to identify shifts in the partisan control of state and local governments, to explore relationships between party loyalty and the cultural backgrounds of voters, and to investigate the attempted curtailment of black voting rights in the South at the end of the nineteenth century.

DIGITAL GENEALOGY
Breakthroughs in historical research often depend on the computer's ability to establish connections among the data in a large body of knowledge. In the mid-1970s, social historian Arthur Imhof took advantage of that facility to reconstruct the patterns of village life in nineteenth-century Germany.

Imhof, a professor at Berlin's Free University, had observed that a fundamental social transformation took place in Germany between the close of the eighteenth century and the second half of the nine-teenth. During that period, both the high birth rates and the high death rates common among villagers fell dramatically. Perhaps the cause was medical, Imhof surmised, and the decline stemmed from the introduction of smallpox vaccine at the turn of the century. Or maybe it was administrative, arising from improved food storage and distribution.

Because the period of Imhof's study ended just before national statistics offices were established in Germany, published data was hard to come by. Imhof therefore turned to parish registers—detailed church records, com-piled since the sixteenth century, that gave the dates of birth, marriage, and death for every parish member, and identified the member's parents, spouse, children, occupation, and cause of death.

Although the registers offered a wealth of information about family lineage, they were limited geographically to the domain of each parish. If Imhof was to monitor what he called geographic micromobility—the movement of individuals for the purpose of marriage, for example, or the movement of families from one parish to another—he would need some means of combining the registers. The university's computer provided it.

Imhof and a team of twelve students fed into a computer database the contents of the registers from eight neigh-boring parishes—facts about nearly 30,000 villagers in all. Imhof then processed the information using a record-linkage program of the sort developed by historian Ian Winchester in 1970. Winchester's program was among the first that could sort and merge into one file the data about an individual or family that was scattered throughout a collection of records. Until the appearance of such programs, wrote David Miller, a history professor at

Carnegie-Mellon University, social historians had accepted as their lot in life "the ceaseless toil of matching thousands of slips of paper on which the baptisms in a parish were recorded, with the marriage and death records of the same individuals, in order to reconstitute families for analysis." Winchester's record-linkage program, however, proved them wrong; by comparing and matching such additional variables as occupation, residence, and first and second initials—and by assigning the same code number to similar-sounding surnames—it was able to link individuals even when they had varied the spelling of a common surname.

Imhof's linkage of the parish registers produced a panoramic picture of 7,000 families residing in a wide area over an extended period of time. Imhof then subjected this statistical portrait to further computer analysis, which revealed such key patterns as the average length of time between births and the number of children who lived past the reproductive years of their parents.

In studying these patterns, Imhof discovered that the decline in mortality had begun with infants and children in the period from 1780 to 1809, and that the life expectancy of adults had begun to rise only decades later. This ruled out medical advances or improved food supply as the cause of the transition, for each of these would have prolonged the life spans of adults at the same time it extended the lives of youngsters. Imhof's computerized process of elimination led him to conclude that the change sprang from a heightened sense of responsibility among parents for the survival of their descendants, brought on, he speculated, by the recognition that family sizes had dwindled over the years.

THE MECHANICS OF TYRANNY

Though a revelation, Imhof's findings did not spark the fires of controversy that have engulfed some projects in quantitative history. In the late 1960s, for example, a group of cliometric scholars overturned the prevailing view that slavery in the American South had been on the verge of collapse just before the Civil War. Instead, the historians reported, the practice had been economically robust.

In 1958, two young Harvard professors, Alfred Conrad and John Meyer, published a pair of landmark papers that demonstrated the feasibility of using mathematical and statistical methods to study the workings of the slave economy. Their research, which examined whether purchases of slaves had been profitable for slaveholders, inspired a large group of economists and historians to reinvestigate the issue. The undertaking was made possible by computers and software that could systematically analyze and interpret statistics on the economics of slavery that had lain squirreled away in archives for decades.

During the 1960s, scores of researchers tracked down details within details of the growth of slavery in America. In the stacks of the National Archives and a number of state archives, they consulted handwritten census statistics about the slave population from 1790 to 1860. At historical societies across the South, they gleaned facts about slave prices and family structure from the business records, family papers, and wills of plantation owners. The researchers even combed the archives of the Genealogical Society of the Mormon Church in Utah, where microfilm copies of probate records gathered from county courthouses yielded still more particulars about the estates of planters whose descendants had joined the Mormon Church.

Using computers, the group then subjected the information from these disparate sources to a series of complex statistical routines. A portrait of the slave economy emerged that, reported economic historians Robert Fogel and Stanley Engerman in their account of the group's work, forced a "radical reinterpretation of American slavery."

Fogel and Engerman's study, published in 1974 as *Time on the Cross,* revealed that slavery on the eve of the war had indeed been highly profitable. The purchase of a slave "yielded rates of return that compared favorably with the most outstanding investment opportunities in manufacturing." Fogel and Engerman also stated that the typical black field hand worked harder than his white counterpart in free farming. Supporting stable slave families had therefore been in the economic interest of planters, and the majority did so.

Perhaps most controversial of all, the cliometricians had subjected data about the food supply on large plantations to statistical tests that showed the nutritional content of the slave diet to be "quite high." From this and related results, they concluded that "the material (not psychological) conditions of the lives of slaves compared favorably with those of free industrial workers." Such findings rankled scholars who, "steeped in the conventional interpretation of the slave system," as Fogel and Engerman characterized them, resisted the idea that a morally repugnant system had spurred rapid economic growth.

A MACHINE FOR TIME TRAVEL

Computers can enliven the teaching of history, too. In 1987, Carnegie-Mellon's David Miller unveiled a computer program called the Great American History Machine (GAHM). The program runs on IBM, Sun Microsystems, and Digital Equipment Corporation work stations, each offering several million bytes of memory, processing speeds faster than one million instructions per second, and high-resolution monitors of nearly one million picture elements (pixels), the tiny dots that form an image on the screen. The work stations are linked to a central bank of data-storage devices by means of a campus-wide computer network that makes vast amounts of information and software readily available to any student.

The GAHM enables students to convert census statistics into detailed maps and charts showing, for example, the changing ethnic mix of the population of Illinois at ten-year intervals from 1840 to the present. Called choropleth maps, such renderings of statistics have been widely used by historians ever since the cartographic technique was pioneered at the turn of the century. Typically, a choropleth map is a county map shaded to represent various economic and demographic data—that is, facts about such things as age, occupation, income, and family size. Although the maps require considerable time and skill to draw by hand, the GAHM generates them effortlessly. A student need only specify a certain formula, and a map

appears on the screen within seconds. For example, the number of foreign-born residents in a community divided by the community's total population would display a map showing districts colored according to percentages of immigrants.

Choropleth maps held a special fascination for Miller. He had observed that historical inquiry centers on the "search for patterns, often in quite a large body of data," and the choropleth map struck him as a medium that would make such patterns readily apparent. In late 1984, aided by grants from Carnegie-Mellon and IBM, Miller and a team of six students began the laborious task of digitizing, or translating into computer-readable binary code, maps of the county boundaries and physical features—railroads, canals, navigable rivers, and mountains—throughout the United States dating back to the 1840s. To accomplish the task, Miller and his students traced the maps' features with a mouse; the signals so generated were then channeled to a sophisticated graphics program known as a drawing editor, which stored the data in a form that could later be recalled to the screen.

As that work progressed, Miller and programmer Stephan Greene also wrote software routines to translate census and election statistics into shadings of the appropriate map sections. Any two maps may be displayed side by side on the screen, letting students compare, for example, the German- and Irish-born populations of a Wisconsin community in 1870. Maps from successive decades may likewise be juxtaposed, indicating, for instance, that the building of a railroad in the Tennessee Valley during the 1850s inflated land values.

Completed in time for a fall 1987 course on U.S. history of the 1800s, the Great American History Machine offered students a powerful tool for unearthing patterns from the past. The program's ability to render digital data in map form helped class members spot such trends as the appearance of "magnet cities"— cities that were settled in advance of the surrounding countryside—west of the Appalachians in the early nineteenth century, the disproportionate growth of industry in the Northeast in the 1840s and 1850s, and the geographic distribution of those who voted for such presidential candidates as the xenophobic Millard Fillmore in 1856 and the secession-minded John Breckinridge in 1860.

IN PURSUIT OF COLUMBUS

Computer-generated maps proved just as vital to the success of the Columbus Research Tool, the computer program that challenged Samuel Eliot Morison's 1942 deduction that Columbus had first set foot in the New World on Watling Island. The puzzle had been posed anew in 1980, when the Society for the History of Discoveries, inspired by the republication of Dutch scholar Pieter Verhoog's 1954 paper that argued in favor of Caicos Island, sponsored a reading of scholarly papers advocating numerous alternative landfalls.

The rekindled debate captured the imagination of National Geographic editor Joseph Judge who, upon reading Columbus's log, had found it to be "filled with quantifiable data—bearings and distances influenced by wind and current and sailing speed." Here, sensed Judge, was the ideal exercise for a computer. Programmed to find a sailing course through the Bahamas that matches the

Reconstructing an Epic Voyage

Charting Columbus's course. Drawn on the nautical chart that spans these pages are two paths proposed for Columbus's sail across the Atlantic. The upper trace shows the Morison track, until recently the most widely accepted route; the lower route, proposed by Judge, was derived after taking currents and leeway into account. To test these and other routes, the geography of the Bahamas was computerized *(below)*, showing islands in yellow and shallows in light blue.

The question of just where in the New World Columbus first set foot has pitted scholar against scholar for centuries. The debate might well have continued for centuries more had not computers cast new light on the issue. Computers, realized *National Geographic* senior editor Joseph Judge, taking up the matter in the 1980s, would provide a way to test innumerable hypotheses with unsurpassed objectivity.

The initial task was to recalculate Columbus's transatlantic track, taking into account for the first time the effects of current and leeway—the sideways skid of a boat on the

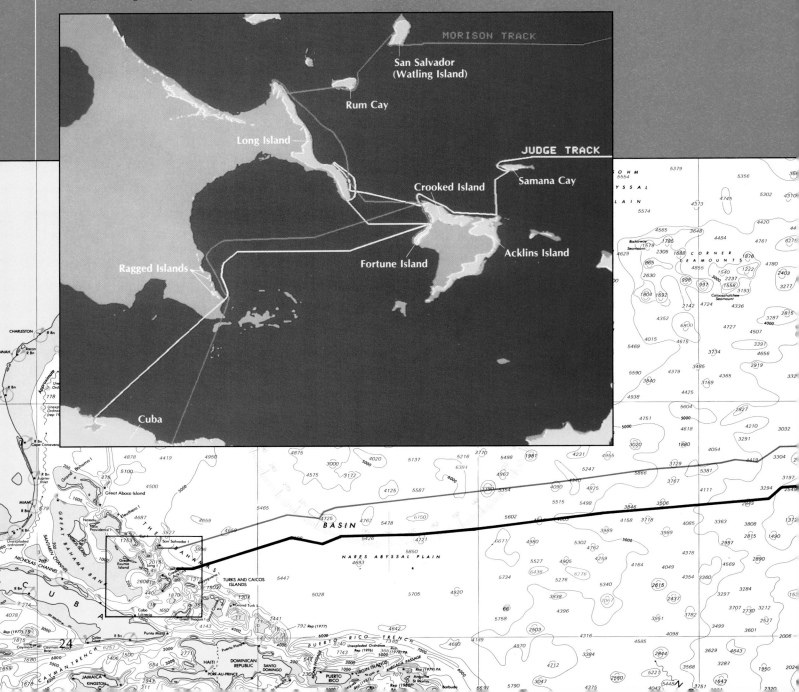

ocean's surface. These tedious calculations, performed by computer, brought Columbus close to the shore of a now-uninhabited island named Samana Cay. This finding clashed with the opinion of historian Samuel Eliot Morison, the most respected Columbus specialist of modern times, who had championed Watling Island, sixty-five miles northwest of Samana Cay, as the landfall. Persuasive proof was therefore required to dislodge the established view.

To test the numerous routes that Columbus might have taken in his exploration of the Bahamas, the locations of islands and shallows were digitized, and hypothetical tracks were plotted on a high-resolution computer screen *(below, left)*. Called the Columbus Research Tool, or CRT, this information bank and the interactive software for using it combine the best of machine and man: The computer's number-crunching prowess and data-storage capacity are joined with human curiosity and powers of deduction. The versatility of the CRT has helped to convince specialists that Samana Cay was indeed where Columbus first planted the flag of Spain in the New World.

Searching the Admiral's Log for Clues

All attempts to retrace Columbus's journey rely on his logbook, the daily record of the flotilla's movements and discoveries. Now surviving only in the form of a copy written by Dominican friar Bartolomé de las Casas in the first half of the sixteenth century, the log records distances covered daily by the fleet and describes the people and places Columbus chanced upon. The page at left recounts the first sighting of land and his subsequent arrival in the New World. Of this event, the log says in essence: "And it was like a small wax candle which rose and moved upward. The Admiral was certain they were near the land. At two hours after midnight, the land appeared, from which they were two leagues. They lowered all the sails and lay to waiting until day." The note in the margin reads, "The Admiral and the others went on the first land of the Indies Friday morning, the 12th of October of 1492."

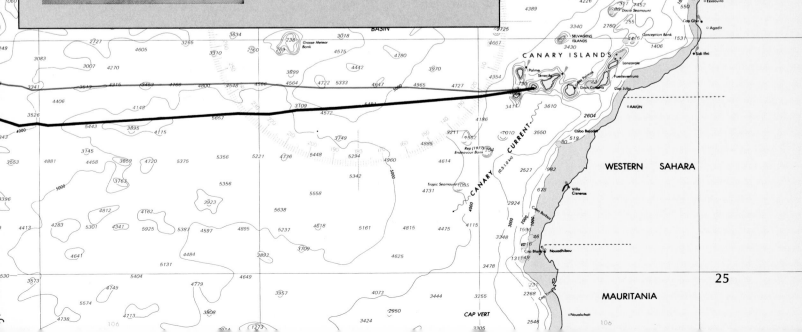

Sailing Routes and Sighting Circles

Containing 14,000 digitized geographic coordinates that represent 342 islands and 235 shallows (treacherous areas Columbus would have avoided), the Columbus Research Tool database provides an ideal medium for the tedious, precise number crunching needed to plot a multitude of routes.

Using details of direction, speed, and distance found in the Columbus log, a researcher can run a proposed track through the CRT to judge its plausibility (below). The task is complicated by the fact that the log is often inconsistent or unclear:

When a direction is cited, for instance, the distance traveled may be missing. Even worse, Columbus was sailing by dead reckoning, that is, he estimated his position by keeping track of time, speed, and direction. Although he was a superb seaman, Columbus's instruments were crude, and his conclusions about his position are known to have been imprecise. The CRT alleviates such problems. For example, when a distance is uncertain, the computer, by testing many possibilities, can help identify the one most likely to be correct.

Another feature of the CRT is its ability to display sighting circles, which indicate the distances at which the tops of the tallest trees on various islands would be visible. This unique feature proves especially valuable in testing Samana Cay as the starting point for Columbus's exploration of the Bahamas.

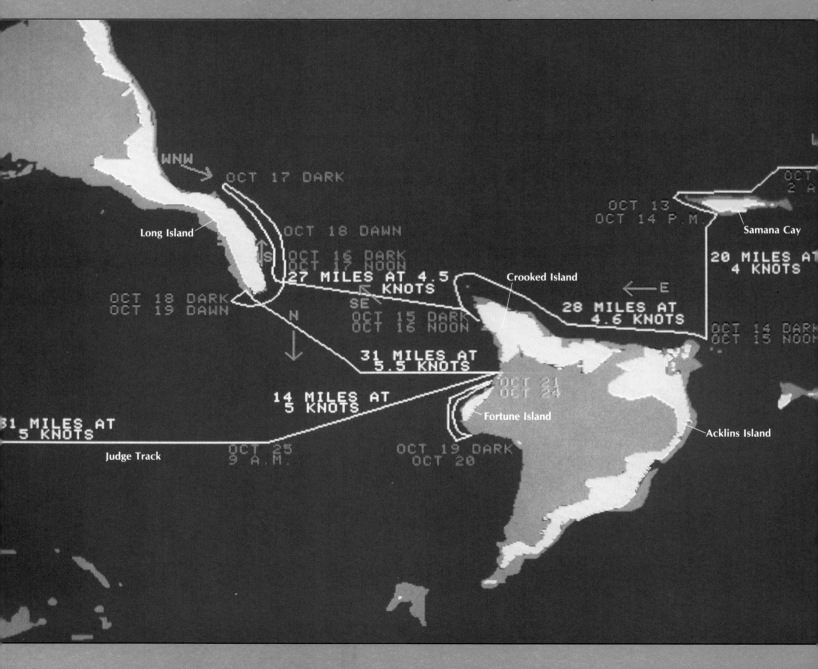

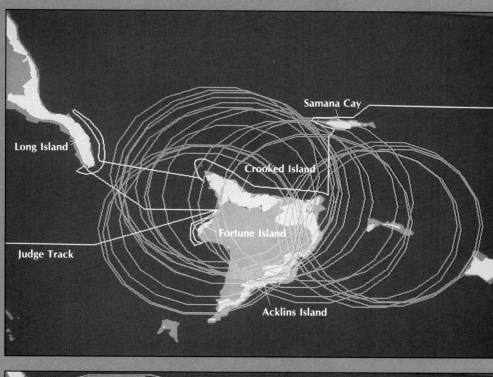

Arcs of visibility. As indicated by sighting circles surrounding the islands south of Samana Cay *(left)*, a sailor leaving the island would see many dozens of land masses dotting the horizon. The sight seems to agree with Columbus's statement in his log that so many islands appeared on leaving his landfall that he had trouble deciding which to sail for. He chose the largest, which the Judge track identifies as the northeast point of Acklins Island.

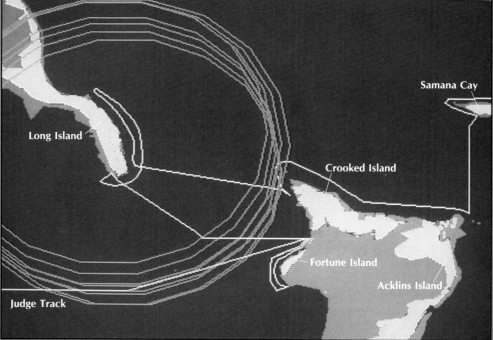

The Cape Verde fix. Sailing from the cluster of islands where he first landed, Columbus noted that a green cape lay seven leagues—approximately twenty nautical miles—to the northwest of his position. The landmark was generally supposed to be Cape Verde, on the southwestern tip of Long Island. Confirming this conclusion, the computer display at left shows sighting circles for the highest points on the cape. The Judge track intersects the circles at just about the position from which Columbus sighted a verdant shore.

◀ **Sailing by computer.** With a digitized database at their disposal, researchers can plot various tracks and test them instantly against information from Columbus's log. In the example at left, the computer screen displays the Judge track as it proceeds from Samana Cay through the Bahamas and ultimately west toward Cuba. The screen also displays various information provided by the log: approximate location by date and time; distances in nautical miles; speeds in knots; and wind directions.

bearings and distances mentioned in the log, "a computer could run the variables out thousands of times." During the process, probable errors in the log could be identified and excluded, and ambiguities could be resolved.

To determine the general location of Columbus's arrival in the region, Judge asked colleague Luis Marden, who had twice sailed his own ketch across the Atlantic, to plot the explorer's transatlantic route. Marden and his wife, Ethel, processed the day-to-day distances, times, and estimated speeds from Columbus's log using two small personal computers, a Tamaya NC-77 and NC-88. The Mardens even calculated the likely effects on Columbus's passage of ocean currents and of his vessels' leeway—the sideways skid of a sailing ship due to wind pressure against the hull and sails. Remarkably, earlier investigators—Morison included—had ignored these factors; their consequences were too time-consuming to calculate with pencil and paper. Marden's figures indicated that the transatlantic track ended about sixty miles south of Watling Island. The nearest land is Samana Cay, a reef-girt island just ten miles away.

Judge next sought to computerize the geography of the region that Columbus had sailed through upon leaving the landfall and continuing west to Cuba. For this he needed someone with a broad range of expertise in cartography, computer graphics, and computer programming. Judge combed the ranks of computer specialists in government and industry without finding the right mix of skills until he happened to contact Robert Lillestrand, a vice president of Control Data Corporation (CDC) in Minneapolis. Lillestrand, an accomplished surveyor and a veteran of two expeditions to the North Pole, had detected and corrected errors in the maps of northern Greenland in 1968. He was also an expert in arctic navigation, having used a computer to study the route taken by explorer Robert Peary to reach the North Pole in 1909. When Judge asked Lillestrand if he knew of anyone sufficiently versed in computer techniques to solve the puzzle of Columbus's passage, Lillestrand responded, "Sure, me."

Working on the Cyber mainframe computer, Lillestrand's associate, programmer Scott Devitt, compiled a cartographic database that incorporated seven maps of the central Bahamas. The coastlines of the region's 342 islands and the boundaries of 235 shallows less than thirty feet deep were recorded in the database as 14,000 geographic coordinates, each requiring six bytes of storage. The resulting digitized maps showed not only the outline of each island that Columbus was likely to have encountered, but also the presence of hazardous waters that he would have been careful to avoid.

With the database in place, another Control Data programmer, Carla Ryti, set out to endow the computer with the ability to analyze a multitude of possible routes and plot each one on the digitized maps. Here the project risked foundering on inconsistencies in the Columbus log. Although Columbus had described the route he followed to reach some of the islands, for others he commented only on the inhabitants and their customs.

This sketchiness of navigational detail, Lillestrand later recalled, ruled out the possibility of developing a "completely automatic system with no human in-

tervention." The CDC vice president and his team therefore made a virtue of necessity, designing the Columbus Research Tool as a "flexible man-machine interface," or interactive computer system, in which researchers are free to choose and test their own alternative routes. Seated before a high-resolution color monitor, a CRT operator electronically "sails" from one point to another, watching the chosen course unfold on the screen as a lengthening zigzag of straight-line segments. The Cyber 170 stores the hypothetical courses and can render a color map of each one on a plotter or can print it as a list of coordinates.

A key feature in judging the validity of any hypothetical route to Cuba is a computer algorithm that members of the CDC team devised through some historical detective work of their own. From the explorer's description of Indian dugout canoes carrying forty men—and allowing one and one-half feet per rower—they reckoned that the canoes must have been about sixty feet long. Estimating that the top forty feet of a tree trunk would have been lopped off as too small to carry rowers, the researchers figured that trees for the canoes must have been about a hundred feet tall.

The height of the trees was then fed into a computer algorithm that the team developed for drawing "sighting circles" centered on islands in the Bahamas. Each circle had a radius equal to the distance at which a lookout perched sixty feet above the waves—the height of the *Santa Maria*'s crow's-nest—could have first spotted trees growing on the highest terrain of each island. Judge used the CRT's sighting algorithm to demonstrate that Columbus must have first set foot in the New World, not on Watling Island, but on tiny Samana Cay *(pages 24-27)*.

COMPUTERS TAKE TO THE FIELD

Like historians, archaeologists have put computers to work in studying all manner of puzzles from the past. No longer equipped merely with trowel, sifter, and tape measure, archaeologists have adopted a variety of sophisticated electronic devices to simplify and speed the collection of data in the field and later to enhance its analysis in the laboratory.

The "dirtiest of disciplines," archaeology offers its practitioners equal parts hope and certainty—hope that a dig will surrender a revealing treasure of ancient civilization, and certainty that it will produce an avalanche of data. Detailed information about each artifact's position in the site, for example, must be meticulously recorded before the objects can be removed from the ground. Precise notes are crucial, for a difference of centimeters in the depth of two buried objects may reflect a span of decades, even centuries, between them. Equal care attends the weighing and measuring of artifacts; this data, like the details of position, helps archaeologists to classify the objects.

Before computers speeded the task, recording the vital statistics of unearthed artifacts consumed nearly half of an archaeologist's time in the field. All that changed, however, with the appearance in the late 1970s of computers small enough to be carried to a dig and rugged enough to endure the dust and heat that often prevail there. Such machines typically stood in the lower ranges of computing power. Yet even a computer that was puny by the standards of the day served archaeologists well. At a prehistoric site in La Quina, France, for example, University of Pennsylvania archaeologist Harold Dibble used a hand-held, battery-powered Hewlett-Packard 71B with just 32,000 bytes of memory to record the positions of 7,000 bones and stone tools that he and his colleagues uncovered in 1986. Despite the 71B's limited capacity, the computer was able to store the locations of as many as 250 artifacts before the data threatened to overflow memory. As that threshold neared, the figures were simply transferred to a more commodious, IBM microcomputer.

By the late 1980s, the increased memory of portable computers offered to make the necessity for such transfers a thing of the past. Laptop computers became available equipped with hard disks that could store as much as twenty megabytes of data—a 600-fold increase over the computers typically used just a decade earlier. In 1988, for example, archaeologist Jim Ebert used a Husky Hawk laptop computer to gather "an entire summer's worth of data" in New Mexico without once having to upload the information to a larger machine.

A host of measuring devices help to minimize the errors and maximize the speed of data collection. Digital scales, for example, can be hooked to a computer to record the weights of excavated artifacts. A second measuring device known as electronic digital calipers can be used to gauge the length, width, and breadth of an artifact, simultaneously transferring the data to a computer for storage and analysis. The electronic digital calipers can also measure the internal dimensions of hollow objects such as pipes, goblets, and cooking vessels.

THE OLD DAYS OF NEW YORK
Nowhere has the computer's speed at data collection been more convincingly demonstrated than during an excavation carried out in the heart of New York City in the winter of 1984. The site, a parking lot paved over rubble, had been slated for development, beginning February 1, as a skyscraper complex to be called the Broad Financial Center. Studies required by the Landmarks Preservation Commission of New York, however, had revealed that beneath the site lay the foundation of the city's first church, erected in 1633, as well as warehouses and other historic buildings of the Dutch West India Company, all built around 1650. Because the developers were eager to start building—every day's delay might cost tens of thousands of dollars in construction-loan interest charges—they gave Greenhouse Consultants, the archaeological company hired for the dig, just nine weeks to complete their work.

Using traditional methods, figured the company's chief archaeologist, Joel W. Grossman, the job would require several months to complete. In November 1983, therefore, while heavy machinery ripped up the parking lot and carted away eight feet of rubble that lay atop the seventeenth-century church and warehouses, Grossman assembled a team of fifty-five archaeologists and

armed them with an array of portable computers and computerized measuring instruments. At the end of December, Grossman's team descended on the site, which was beset by heavy snows and winter winds. Before beginning work, the team had to erect 1,600 square feet of heated shelters to shield themselves, the fragile artifacts, and the computer equipment from the elements.

The jewel in this technological crown was an infrared version of a transit, the instrument that a surveyor squints through to fix an object's position. In less than five seconds, this computerized instrument measures and calculates an artifact's three-dimensional coordinates, a process that takes hours with standard surveying gear.

In use, the infrared transit must first be programmed with its own location at the dig site. Called the absolute position, this location, once established, remains the same for the duration of the work. After the preliminaries, the location of any artifact is determined simply by sighting an artifact through the instrument. Inside the transit, a device known as a theodolite then measures and records two angles—the bearing (horizontal angle) and angle of depression (vertical angle) to the artifact. Finally, a component of the transit called an electronic distance meter (EDM) flashes a pulse of infrared light at a reflective prism placed on the artifact. From the interval between sending out the pulse and detecting the reflection, the EDM calculates the distance to the artifact with an error of less than one inch per mile.

A microprocessor inside the transit combines these three measurements—the two angles and the distance—to compute the artifact's position in a three-dimensional grid imposed on the site. As the readings are made, they are sent by cable to a portable computer—an Epson HX-20 laptop, in the case of the New York excavation—that stores them for later transfer into a database containing coordinates for every artifact retrieved from the site. The swiftness of such a scheme enabled the archaeologists at the New York dig to complete their work three days ahead of schedule. Among the 43,318 artifacts they inventoried were 21,611 objects predating 1725. The finds included a seal belonging to the first British customs collector in colonial New York, as well as a mix of objects—including a quantity of wampum—documenting that the early Dutch settlers had conducted a lively trade with Indians at the site.

THE CONSUMMATE DETECTIVE

Like a prospector after gold, archaeologists in search of relics have to know where to dig. They have therefore put computers to work in hopes of predicting the locations of sites still to be discovered. The most sophisticated result of their efforts is a forecasting tool known as a Geographic Information System (GIS), a rich database containing detailed maps of an area of archaeological interest. The maps show known historic sites and structures, the extent of any archaeological fieldwork completed or under way, and the boundaries of all modern towns and cities in the region; in many instances, the maps also encompass road networks, both ancient and modern. To this information is added a profusion of geographical data—soil type, vegetation patterns, exposure to sun, sources of water, and view shed (the availability of vantage points for spotting enemies or game). Programmed with details of an ancient way of life—farming or hunting, for example—a computer may be able to spot places well suited to such civilizations, helping archaeologists to discover new sites.

Stuffing information into a GIS is a job as varied as the sources of the data itself. Transferring detail from maps into the database may be accomplished by a device known as a coordinate digitizer, which tags map features with coordinates expressed in latitude and longitude, and converts them into a form suitable for computer manipulation and display. Such details may likewise be digitized by video camera or by optical scanner, a machine that passes a light-sensitive head repeatedly across a map or chart, capturing the details in narrow strips that a computer can reassemble into a digital rendition of the original.

Some sources supply information in computer form, eliminating the need to digitize it. The Defense Mapping Agency's Topographic Center, for example, and the U.S. Geological Survey make their data available on disks and magnetic tapes. Other computer-ready information comes from private satellite companies—notably the French SPOT and the American LANDSAT—whose orbiting observatories use photographic instruments sensitive to infrared radiation as well as visible light to collect data on soil types and vegetation worldwide.

Information from these disparate sources has been built up in Geographic Information Systems for areas of diverse archaeological interest. In 1985, for example, archaeologist Kenneth Kvamme of the University of Arizona compiled a GIS encompassing 550 square kilometers of Colorado occupied by prehistoric bison-hunting tribes. He included ten aspects of the environment in his GIS, including elevation, slope, availability of natural shelter, view shed, and sources of water. Comparing the locations of 269 known Indian settlements in the region in terms of these variables, the GIS revealed that the area's original inhabitants had settled along the rims of canyons an average 600 feet above seasonal streams, facts that Kvamme used to narrow his search for additional settlements.

Archaeologist Scott Madry, who first used a GIS to locate buried Roman villas in central France in the late 1970s, has continued to study the region using a GIS in his computer laboratory near Jackson, Mississippi. "With access to a GIS," said Madry, "we may soon be able to locate individual field sites without ever leaving our laboratory. Although much of our fieldwork in France ended in 1980, I'm still working there, in effect, because I've captured that research area as a digital database."

NUMERICAL CHIMERAS

There is a third realm—that of mathematics—in which puzzles of long standing are bowing to the computer. Some of them are so tangled, so intractable that they have spawned a new branch of mathematics called complexity theory. And the search for solutions to complex problems, wrote mathematician Paul Hoffman in 1988, has become "the hottest pursuit in theoretical computer science."

A problem qualifies as complex when the amount of computer time required to solve it is impossibly large. A notorious example is the dilemma of the traveling salesman: Given a network of cities, find the shortest possible round-trip route that will pass through each city only once. The traveling-salesman problem (TSP) has captivated complexity theorists because it may hold the key to unlocking solutions for an entire family of more practical problems: the routing of a fleet of school buses, for example, the scheduling of National Football League games, or even the arrangement of wires and transistors on an integrated circuit.

The intractability of such complex problems as the traveling salesman's quandary, notes Richard Karp, a pioneer of complexity theory, stems from a phenomenon known as combinatorial explosion. This feature distinguishes complex problems from those that are merely difficult to solve. When the traveler is slated to visit four cities, for example, the number of possible routes is just three. But with each city that is added to the itinerary, the number of possible combinations exhibits phenomenal growth: For five cities, the total is 12; at six, the number is 60; and with ten cities, there are 181,440 ways to visit them all.

For computers assigned to solve the TSP, the combinatorial explosion spells trouble. Every computer algorithm—an explicit, step-by-step procedure guaranteed to yield a precise solution—that mathematicians have been able to devise for the problem undergoes some form of combinatorial explosion, which involves an exponentially growing number of steps. Even for a computer fast enough to evaluate one million sales trips per second—a rate that far exceeded the speed of supercomputers in the late 1980s— the "brute-force enumeration" of all possible tours through twenty cities would take more than a thousand years; for twenty-five cities, it would take approximately 10 million years. A computer 1,000 times faster would be little help; adding just one or two cities to the sales representative's itinerary—or to the number of stops on a school-bus route— would offset the increased speed.

SAVING THE LIFE OF WILLY LOMAN
Karp became intrigued with the TSP shortly after joining IBM's Yorktown Heights Research Center in 1959. Karp and IBM colleague Michael Held, in a bid to spare

their IBM 7090 mainframe computer from searching through every one of the problem's "furiously growing number of possibilities," began to investigate a set of mathematical expedients known as branch-and-bound methods. The particular branch-and-bound method they devised, Karp later recalled, "allowed us to prune the search severely," and in 1967 the two men computed an optimum tour for sixty-five cities. "I don't think any of my theoretical results have provided as great a thrill as the sight of the numbers pouring out of the computer on the

Circles and lines in this computerized cross section of an archaeological dig at La Quina, France, represent prehistoric stone tools and bones recovered from the site in 1986. Colors distinguish the different civilizations that occupied the site. The steep face of the bluff where the site lies accounts for the absence of artifacts on the left side of the picture. A white arrow designates an artifact for which an archaeologist seeks additional information—its dimensions and weight, for example. A touch of a button brings the data to the screen.

night Held and I first tested our bounding method," wrote Karp. Yet the Held-Karp method did not eliminate the combinatorial explosion, only slowed its growth.

In the early 1970s, mathematicians Shen Lin and Brian Kernighan of Bell Labs became the leading prosecutors of the quest for a computational shortcut to the problem. Rather than seeking a strict, algorithmic solution, the two experimented with heuristic methods—mathematical equivalents of the rules of thumb that humans use to arrive at workable, though not necessarily optimum, solutions to problems.

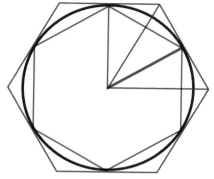

To calculate pi (a circle's circumference divided by its diameter) without measuring the circle's girth, Greek mathematician Archimedes assigned a value of one to the diameter. Then, as shown at left, he used the geometry of triangles and the radius of the circle to compute the perimeters of two six-sided figures, one drawn inside the circle and one outside. Both the circumference and pi lie between these values. By increasing to ninety-six the number of sides in the polygons—and thus making them nearly coincide with the circle—Archimedes narrowed the value of pi to four decimal places.

The centerpiece of the Lin-Kernighan approach was a "local-improvement algorithm" that instructed the labs' GE-635 mainframe computer to generate a random tour of cities and then cut the route into sections. The computer then tried to shorten the journey through each section by applying an algorithmic approach to the relatively few cities within it. The result was a reasonably efficient itinerary—though perhaps not the shortest one—to all the cities.

Using this method, Lin and Kernighan solved tours for as many as 110 cities in less than twenty-five seconds, with the program's observed execution time growing at a very manageable rate. Only the limited computer-storage capacity of the day kept them from calculating tours with a higher number of way points.

Because the Lin-Kernighan method provided satisfactory solutions to practical instances of the TSP, it proved of enormous appeal to business people, scientists, and engineers. In 1976, for example, the U.S. Bureau of Fisheries used the Lin-Kernighan algorithm to find a shorter route for the crew it was sending out to sample fish populations at 300 separate points in the Gulf of Mexico each day.

While Lin and Kernighan were developing their heuristic approach, Karp had continued to work on the problem, but his duties as director of the University of California's newly formed Computer Science Division had kept him from concentrating on the task. In 1975, Karp took a sabbatical to work on the probabilistic analysis of algorithms, a field of study that included the TSP. One result of his labors that year was a simple "divide-and-conquer" approach to solving enormously large instances of the TSP. Although Karp downplayed the strategy as no more than a "theoretical curiosity," it represented an innovative angle of attack toward a complex problem.

Postulating that the cities in large TSPs are randomly distributed like the points in a rectangular plane, Karp wrote a computer algorithm that divided the rectangle into several smaller rectangles, each containing a much smaller number of cities than the total. The algorithm then computed an optimal tour through the cities in each rectangle; finally, the algorithm performed what Karp called "a kind of local surgery" to eliminate redundant visits to cities located on the borders between rectangles, and combined the constituent tours into a complete one. Karp's divide-and-conquer strategy, as well as the other solutions that he had devised during a quarter century of work on such puzzlelike problems as the TSP, earned him the Association of Computing Machinery's prestigious Turing Award in 1985. Though superior to the Lin-Kernighan method, Karp's solution cannot reveal the shortest possible route. The traveling-salesman problem has therefore continued to present an irresistible challenge to mathematicians and computer scientists the world over.

NEW RECIPES FOR PI

Of all mathematical puzzles, the one that has absorbed scholars the longest is the calculation of pi. Not only does this constant equal the ratio of a circle's circumference to its diameter, it also describes the ratio of a circle's area to the square of its radius, and it can be used to predict the probability that a randomly selected whole number will have no repeated prime divisors.

The first man to analyze pi was most probably the Greek mathematician Archimedes of Syracuse, who lived in the third century BC. Using a system of inscribed and circumscribed polygons *(left)*, Archimedes proved that the value of pi lay somewhere between $3^{10}/_{71}$ and $3\frac{1}{7}$. Archimedes' method was perhaps more significant than the results it produced, for it established the possibility of calculating pi in a purely mathematical fashion, without recourse to direct measurements of a circle's circumference, area, or diameter.

In the seventeenth century, English mathematician Sir Isaac Newton used a mathematical technique of his own devising to calculate fifteen digits of pi. Afterward, Newton admitted to a colleague that he was "ashamed to tell you to how many figures I carried these computations, having no other business at the time." Newton's answer: 3.14159265358979. . . .

With the appearance of electronic digital computers in the 1940s, the calculation of pi became a benchmark computation that was used to show off the power—or simply the reliability—of new machines. One of the first computer calculations of pi was made by the vacuum-tube ENIAC, which in June of 1949 figured pi to 2,037 decimal places. In 1958 an IBM 704 computed 10,000 digits, and a CDC 7600 reached the million-digit mark in 1973.

Like Newton, today's digit hunters admit that their pursuit may have little practical application. They hope, however, that the decimal expansion of pi may reveal some significant pattern—a preponderance of zeros and ones, for example—in the upper reaches of the digit string. Such a finding would prove that, contrary to current mathematical conjecture, the digit string of pi is not a random sequence.

The exploration of pi acceler-

Indian mathematical genius Srinivasa Ramanujan recorded his complex theorems in private journals that he titled notebooks. The pages were covered with mathematical propositions, offered without proof and written in a manner that baffled most mathematicians *(right)*. Nearly seventy-five years passed before the notebooks yielded their treasure of revolutionary methods for reckoning pi that, when written into computer programs, made possible the calculation of pi to an unprecedented degree of precision.

ated in the 1980s with the emergence of new supercomputers—and the rediscovery of some old equations among the work of Srinivasa Ramanujan. Born in the small Indian city of Erode in 1887, Ramanujan received little formal training in mathematics. Yet by the age of twenty-three he had written a body of theorems whose clarity and elegance would take the mathematical world by storm. In 1913, Ramanujan sent 120 of the formulas, a mere sample of his work, to prominent British mathematician Godfrey H. Hardy at Trinity College in Cambridge. Astonished by the originality of the Indian's mathematics, Hardy invited Ramanujan to study at Cambridge.

Ramanujan left India for Britain aboard a steamer in March of 1914. It was a move that would seal both his fame and his fate. Ramanujan won recognition for his mathematical research at Cambridge, but England's war-rationed diet made it difficult for him to observe the strict vegetarianism dictated by his Hindu religion, and in the spring of 1917, he fell victim to a vitamin deficiency that claimed his life three years later.

Among the formulas that would secure Ramanujan's fame were some extraordinary methods for calculating pi. These methods were not fully appreciated until the early 1980s, when mathematician Bruce Berndt of the University of Illinois began deciphering Ramaunjuan's peculiar coded notations. The methods were of special interest to brothers Jonathan and Peter Borwein, both professors of mathematics at Dalhousie University in Halifax, Nova Scotia.

The Borweins had been examining the properties of pi for several years. Upon learning of Ramanujan's equations, the Borweins converted them into a set of iterative computer algorithms—so called because they repeatedly perform the same sequence of arithmetic operations, with the output of one cycle furnishing the input for the next—that are capable of quadrupling or even quintupling the number of digits in pi with each repetition. In 1986, NASA computer consultant David Bailey used two of the Borweins' algorithms in a computer program that pushed the value of pi to a record-breaking 29,360,000 decimal places. The two algorithms ran sequentially, with the first performing the computation and the second checking its results. Although Bailey's program required twenty-eight hours of processing time on a Cray-2 supercomputer, the Borwein algorithm needed just twelve iterations to calculate pi to this unprecedented degree of accuracy. Shortly thereafter, Tokyo University professor Yasumasa Kanada extended the value of pi to more than 201 million digits.

To arrive at such a prodigious string of numbers is only the first step, however. With every refinement of pi's value, mathematicians and computer scientists subject the newly computed digit string to a battery of statistical tests, typically embodied in a pattern-matching computer program that examines the occurrence of all double integers—11, for example, or 22—within a stretch of the digit string, and from this predicts the frequency of future repetitions. Whenever the program detects a deviation from the incidence thus projected, it flags that portion of the digit string for further analysis.

Computer analysis has failed to turn up a pattern in the digit string of pi, but that may be only because computers have yet to search long enough or far enough. Iterating the Borweins' algorithms fifteen times would calculate pi to more than two billion digits, a quantity that would occupy mathematicians and their computers for many years in the search for a pattern in pi.

Computer Sleuths in the Museum

The study of art and historical artifacts produces its share of puzzles and questions. How old is this piece of pottery? Was this painting ever restored? Is this sculpture a priceless masterpiece—or is it a worthless fake? Art historians and critics have traditionally relied on often-subjective judgments of style, the examination of such external evidence as letters and diaries, and even their own intuitive skills in the hunt for plausible answers. But as computers have become more proficient at collecting and analyzing information in all sorts of forms, the field of artistic investigation has become a far more exacting discipline.

In conjunction with a diverse range of sophisticated scientific detecting and measuring equipment, computers offer the experts new ways of looking at artworks and thereby help uncover many hidden truths. Although the techniques vary, most involve a minute, sometimes subatomic, examination of a work. Once the data is converted into the digital language of computers, different computational procedures can be applied, from image processing to statistical analysis, to reveal details of workmanship or distinctions in style or composition that would otherwise escape notice.

As·well as helping scholars date and classify artifacts, unmask forgeries, detect restorations, and better understand the artistic process, high-tech methods are proving indispensable in the field of art preservation. Precision computer-guided examination and monitoring of deterioration are pointing conservators toward more effective means of protecting invaluable relics.

The following pages present a gallery of computerized detective techniques applied to an assortment of artistic media, from parchment and paint to wood, metal, and clay.

A Watchful Eye on the Cherished Past

Although the contents of such hallowed documents as the Declaration of Independence, the Constitution, and the Bill of Rights are indelibly etched in the nation's consciousness, the documents themselves are by no means immune from physical deterioration. Conservators have gone to great lengths to preserve these relics, sealing them in specially constructed glass cases that protect against the deleterious effects of sunlight and air. And to ensure that the fragile parchments are being adequately safeguarded, a computerized imaging system has been devised to monitor their condition and detect any changes that might warrant an adjustment in preservation techniques.

The camera that carries out inspections of the documents incorporates a charge-coupled device (CCD), similar to those used on telescopes to record the extremely faint light of distant stars. Each image created by the CCD comprises almost a million pixels, or picture elements, per square inch. The CCD digitally records the brightness at each pixel by counting the electrons excited in its silicon surface, when struck by photons of light. So sensitive is the CCD that it can distinguish a thousand gradations of brightness, each representing a different shade of gray.

Images captured by the CCD camera are stored in a computer as sets of numbers, which can then be converted by an image-processing system into photographs such as those at bottom right. To determine if changes have occurred in a document, the computer is programmed to make pixel-by-pixel comparisons of images taken at different times. In this way, even the most minute signs of deterioration can be detected long before they are visible to the naked eye.

Precision imaging. The computer-controlled camera for photographing historic documents is supported on tracks above a granite-and-steel examining table that eliminates blurring vibrations. The camera scans selected patches of a document in finely controlled steps, with each step yielding a small portion of total image. In subsequent examinations, the computer re-creates the alignment of camera and document to within one thousandth of a millimeter, making possible precise comparisons of images.

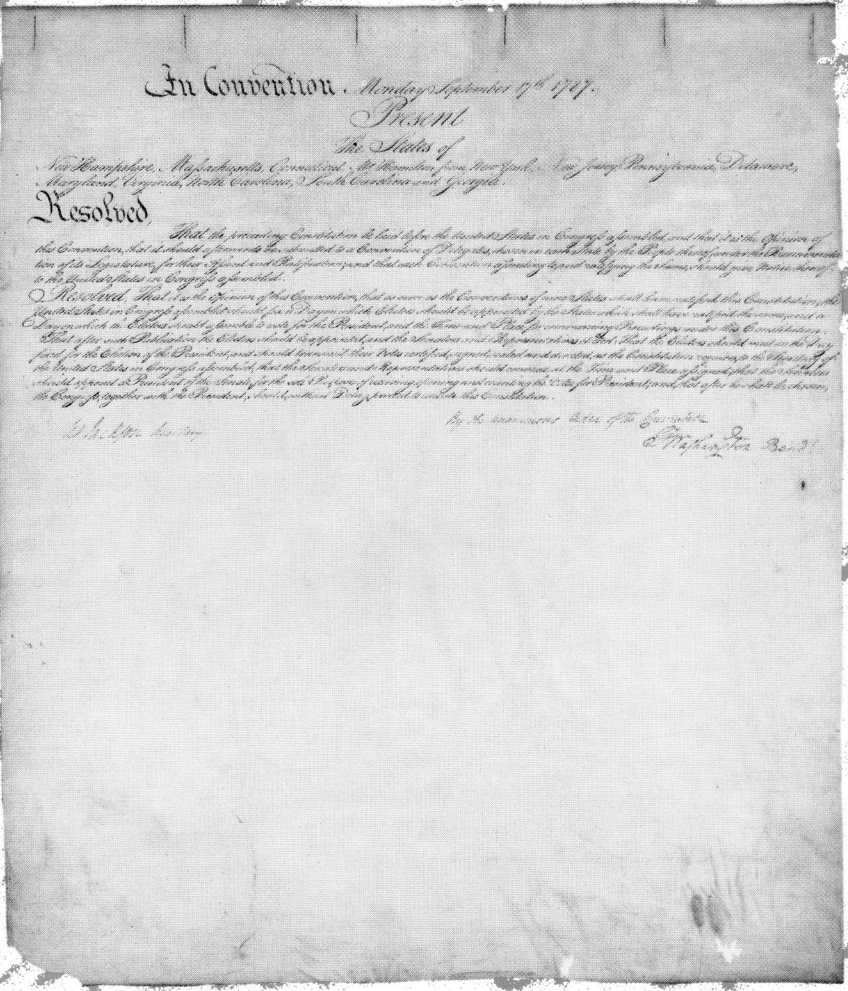

In Convention. Monday September 17th 1787.

Present

The States of

New Hampshire, Massachusetts, Connecticut, Mr. Hamilton from New York, New Jersey, Pennsylvania, Delaware, Maryland, Virginia, North Carolina, South Carolina and Georgia.

Resolved,

A timeworn piece of history. This letter, signed by George Washington as president of the Constitutional Convention, presents the new United States Constitution to the Congress and details the procedures for its ratification and for the election of a first U.S. president. Like the Constitution itself, the letter was essentially unprotected until 1952, when archivists enclosed it in an airtight glass case. The computerized monitoring system regularly photographs selected patches of the parchment, looking for evidence of fading or other forms of deterioration.

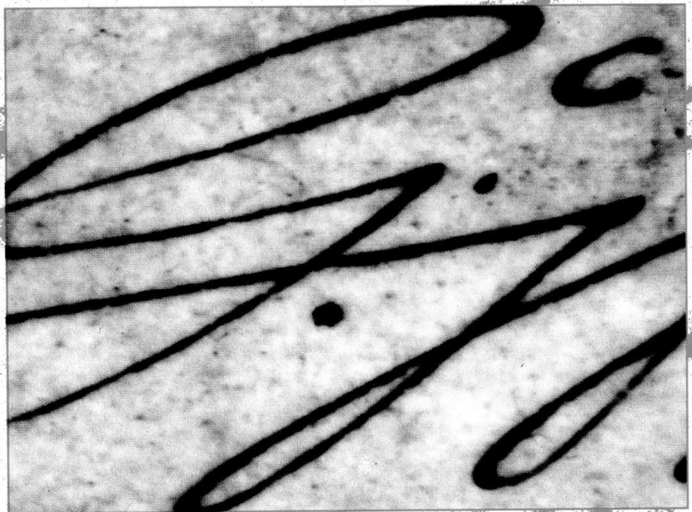

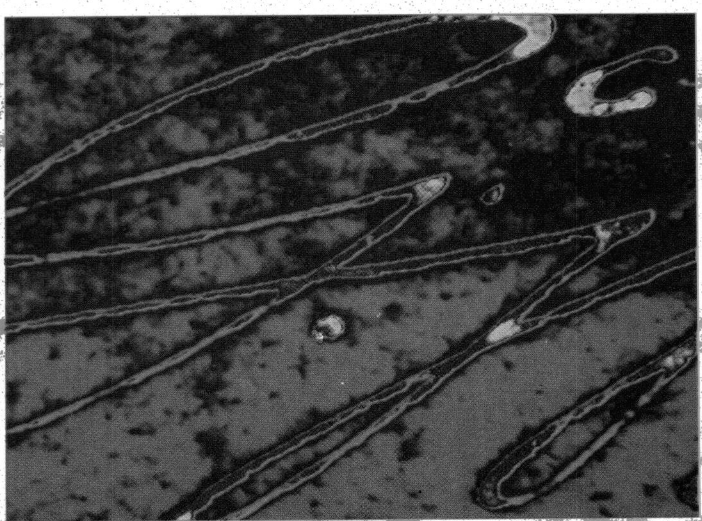

Computerized closeups. The electronically recorded images above and at right, showing a portion of Washington's signature, consist of hundreds of thousands of pixels apiece. False coloring *(right)* reveals fine details that would otherwise be imperceptible to the eye. The signature, which appears a uniform black at left, actually varies in shade, with yellow, green, and blue representing progressively lighter sections.

Peering beneath a Painting's Surface

Art historians have always been fascinated not only by the final product of an artist's vision but by the process of creation itself, how ideas develop and sometimes change in the artist's mind. Surviving drawings can furnish interesting information about the genesis of a painted work, but new imaging and computer techniques have uncovered much more intriguing objects of study. Scholars can now analyze the preliminary sketches that served as guides for the final work and actually lie hidden beneath the painted surface.

Exposing these images by nondestructive methods involves a technique known as infrared reflectography, which relies on the ability of infrared light to penetrate most pigments and, in effect, see through to what lies below. Once beyond the surface colors, the light is absorbed by carbon-based materials, such as the charcoal or black chalk used for sketching, but is reflected by the white paint with which some artists prepared their canvases. The result is a pattern of reflection and absorption that can be detected by a specially designed camera and accurately represents the hidden sketch.

To capture the finest possible detail, the camera focuses on one small section of the painting at a time. The dozens of separate exposures are then assembled like a mosaic to show the entire work. The computer's role is to digitize the images and process the data to correct for distortions. Further processing blends the edges of the mosaic sections to produce a seamless picture.

Penetrating with light. To reveal the sketch beneath a painting, a lamp bathes the work with infrared light, which penetrates the overlying layers of pigment. Beams that strike the dark lines of the sketch are absorbed *(top arrow)*, while those hitting the white background are reflected *(bottom arrow)* toward a special camera that filters out everything but the infrared light. A computer then digitizes the infrared signal *(blue stepped arrow)*, and the processed image is displayed on a video monitor.

A detailed sketch. At left is the original *Arrival in Bethlehem*, painted in the sixteenth century by a Flemish artist known only as Master L.C. The computerized view of the underlying sketch *(below)* reveals an extraordinary amount of preparatory drawing that took place before any paint was applied. Some details in the sketch, such as the walking stick, bowl, and cloth to the right of the figure on the bridge, were omitted in the final work.

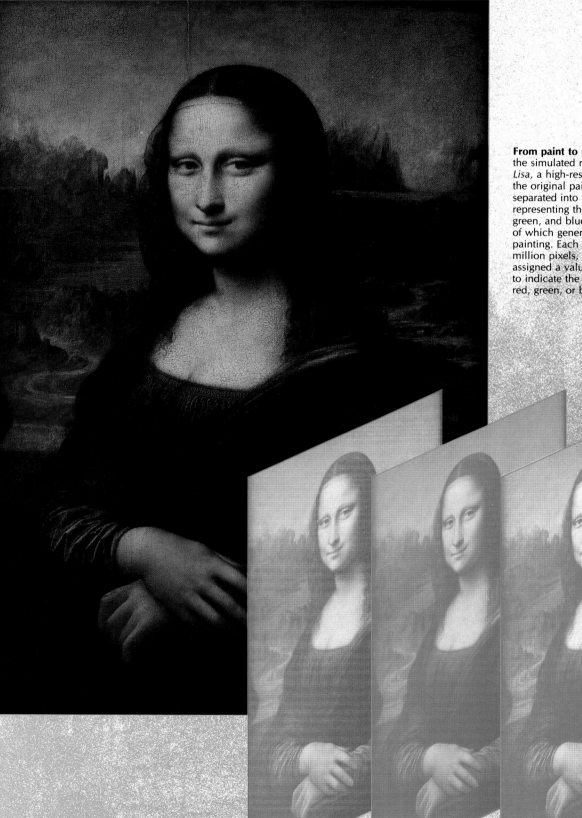

From paint to pixels. As a first step in the simulated restoration of the *Mona Lisa*, a high-resolution photograph of the original painting *(left)* was separated into three digital images representing the primary colors red, green, and blue *(below)*, combinations of which generate all the hues in the painting. Each image consists of six million pixels, and each pixel was assigned a value ranging from 0 to 255 to indicate the level of brightness of red, green, or blue at that point.

A Masterpiece Digitally Restored

Perhaps the most celebrated painting in the world, the *Mona Lisa* is not now what it used to be. In the more than 450 years since Leonardo da Vinci created the portrait, its varnish has yellowed, and myriad tiny cracks have marred its surface. In the absence of an actual physical restoration, scientists have turned to computers to give them some idea of the glories time may have obscured in this still-glorious work.

As always, the computer would perform its magic by manipulating numbers, so the first task was to transform the *Mona Lisa*'s image into digital form. Once that was done, precise measurements could be made of the intensity of color at each of many pixel points. Several different image-processing techniques were then applied, similar to those used to clarify and enhance astronomical images beamed back to earth from deep in space. Although the procedures varied, the basic tactic in each case was to alter the digitized values representing the painting according to an algorithm specially formulated to achieve a particular result, such as eliminating cracks or compensating for the dulling effects of old varnish. One of the most interesting revelations was that certain areas—including the famous enigmatic smile—had been retouched or abrasively cleaned at some point in the painting's history and may no longer appear exactly as Leonardo fashioned them.

Varnish removal by the numbers. In order to compensate for the dulling effect of the thick layer of yellowed varnish covering the painting, a sample of similarly discolored varnish was analyzed to determine the factor by which it muted each of the three primary colors. A computer was then programmed to multiply the value of each blue pixel by 2.5 and each green pixel by 5, and to leave the red pixels as they were—in effect restoring each pixel to its original, unvarnished brightness. The final result, once the three digital images were recombined, was a more vivid, natural-looking image *(above)*.

Uncovering evidence of a touch-up. Further manipulation of image data identified areas of earlier repair by enhancing the thousands of cracks in the surface of the painting. The entire image was divided into squares of thirty-one pixels on a side, and an average intensity value was computed for each square. Pixels that deviated greatly from the average in their group, such as those representing the dark cracks, were intensified to emphasize the deviation and make the cracks more apparent. By exaggerating differences between large and small— presumably more recent—cracks, the processed image *(above)* revealed areas around the mouth and eyes that had been painted over, or touched up, sometime after the original work was done.

An ingrained history. Known as the *Deposition,* this panel from a much larger work carved by Adriaen van Wesel in the mid-fifteenth century depicts Christ's body being lowered from the cross. A view of the bottom edge *(below)* shows faint traces of the growth rings of the tree from which the panel was cut. Minute examination revealed a sequence of seventy rings that enabled researchers to date the tree and thus arrive at an approximation of the age of the sculpture.

A Tree-Ring Approach to Dating Art

Determining when a work of art was created can sometimes be quite a challenge. When the medium is wood, valuable clues can often be garnered by analyzing patterns in the wood's growth rings.

Using a method known as dendrochronology, or tree-ring dating, researchers have been able to date with reasonable precision such artworks as the sculpture at left by Adriaen van Wesel. The works of this fifteenth-century Dutch carver had never before been accurately chronicled.

In order to date a particular piece of wood, the pattern of its yearly growth rings must be compared with a reference pattern, known as a master chronology. This guide to the history of a particular wood details the average widths of growth rings for the type of tree being studied, in some cases dating back thousands of years from the present. Computers have greatly simplified the task of developing master chronologies, digitally storing readings from hundreds of trees, and continually computing updated averages based on new findings. Computers also play a role in matching specific samples to the chronology: Because an individual pattern will never duplicate the chronology's pattern precisely, statistical tests—easily enacted by computers—help determine when the patterns are sufficiently similar to indicate a possible match. The ultimate judgment is then left to the skill and experience of the researcher.

Once the wood has been accurately dated, other factors—such as whether any of the outermost rings appear to be missing, or how long wood was typically aged after felling—must be taken into account before a final estimation of the age of the artwork itself can be made.

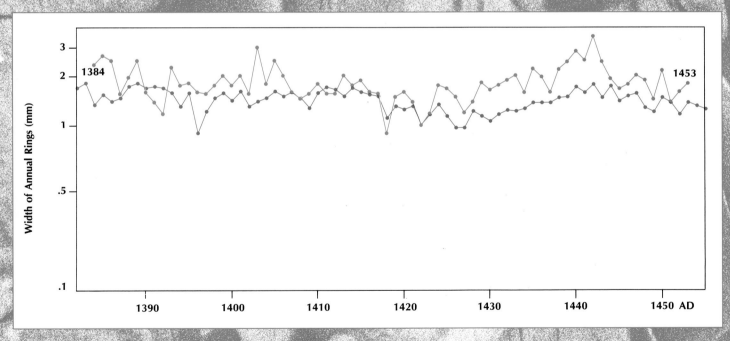

Matching a master chronology. The two traces on the chart above show the average tree-ring widths in millimeters for Polish oak (*blue line*) from the 1380s to the 1450s and the actual ring widths from the underside of the *Deposition (red line)*. A computer compiled the so-called master chronology for Polish oak by processing measurements from hundreds of individual specimens. The *Deposition* pattern was then statistically compared with different portions of the master chronology until a match was found. Although the widths for specific years rarely coincide, a high percentage of parallel variation—in which the two patterns follow the same general trends of increase or decrease—indicates that the sample has been properly dated.

X-ray evidence. As illustrated in the two simplified diagrams below, an atom's electrons *(white)* circle the nucleus *(blue)* in different orbits, or shells. Each shell represents a different electron energy level, with the most energetic electrons in the outermost shell. When an x-ray beam strikes an atom *(top drawing, white arrow)*, it dislodges an inner-shell electron *(red)*, placing the atom in an unstable, or excited, state. To return the atom to a stable state, an electron from a higher shell drops down to fill the gap in the inner shell *(bottom drawing)*. As it does so, it loses energy, which is emitted from the atom as an x-ray *(wavy line)* at a wavelength equivalent to the difference in energy levels between the two shells. This difference is characteristic of the atom and reveals its identity.

Atomic Analysis of an Artwork's Makeup

The skill of great artists is sometimes rivaled by the deftness of imitators and forgers. As a result, art experts are often hard-pressed to distinguish the genuine masterpiece from the clever copy. But a careful, computer-assisted examination of an artwork's elemental components—the precise chemistry of a painting's pigments or the exact combination of metals in a sculpture—will provide hard evidence if the piece is a fake. The same techniques also help distinguish between original work and later additions or restorations.

The bronze statue shown here of Bacchus and a faun, by an unknown Italian sculptor of the late fifteenth or early sixteenth century, is an interesting case in point. It once included a fig leaf that experts suspected could be attributed to the prudishness of a later age. Both the fig leaf and the main sculpture were tested by a complex process known as x-ray fluorescence spectroscopy, which reveals constituent elements on the basis of their atomic structure. The principle behind the procedure is that when metals are bombarded by an x-ray beam, the atoms of particular elements will radiate, or fluoresce, at characteristic x-ray wavelengths that can be measured by special detecting instruments. Because alloys such as bronze may contain traces of many different elements, a multitude of signals barrages the sensing equipment, making computer processing and analysis a must.

Once each signal was pinpointed and matched with a particular element, researchers were able to confirm the theory that the fig leaf on the Bacchus sculpture was made from a different alloy. The leaf was removed to restore the work to its original condition.

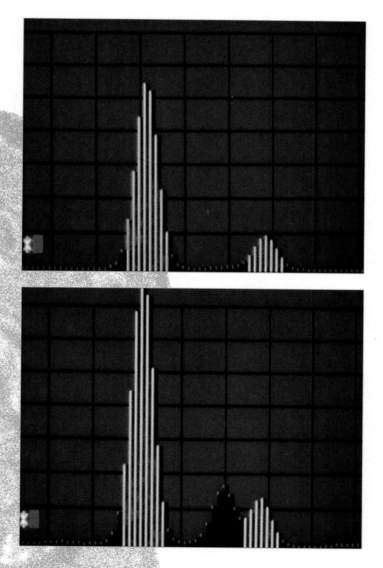

A graphic portrayal of elements. The two graphs at right, produced by a computer from data gathered by x-ray fluorescence spectroscopy, reveal differences in the elemental makeup of the Bacchus sculpture *(top)* and a fig leaf once attached to it *(bottom)*. The horizontal axis of each graph represents the energy level of emitted x-rays, which indicates an element's identity; the vertical axis represents the x-rays' intensity, which denotes the proportion of a particular element in a given sample. The two groups of yellow lines in the top graph show two levels of x-ray energy signifying the presence of copper in the bronze of the statue. The bottom graph reveals a greater proportion of copper in the fig leaf and the presence of zinc *(black)*, not found in the main sculpture.

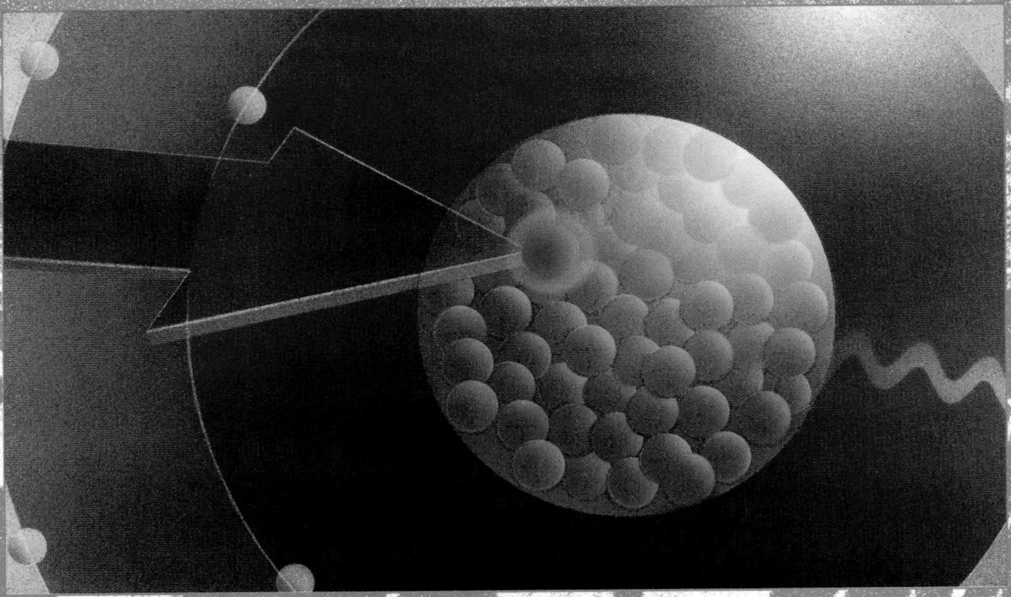

Neutron bombardment. The chemical composition of ancient pottery fragments can be determined by neutron activation analysis, a process that relies on the tendency of some types of atoms to become radioactive. As illustrated at left, when a beam of neutrons (*arrow*) is fired at a sample, a single neutron is absorbed into the atom's nucleus, making the atom radioactive. The atom begins to decay and gives off gamma rays (*wavy line*). Because many elements have unique gamma-ray sighatures, analysis of the rays reveals which elements are present in the sample.

Modern Methods for Ancient Artifacts

The agora, or marketplace, of Athens was for many centuries before the birth of Christ a bustling center of commerce and has thus proved a rich source of artifacts for archaeologists. Fragments of pottery from several different eras and locales litter the various excavation sites in the agora, making classification a complicated task in which computers have been particularly helpful.

Portable computers have quickly become one of the excavator's most prized tools, greatly facilitating the process of recording on the spot the precise location of findings—often an important clue in identifying specimens. But even more sophisticated assistance takes place back in the research laboratory. As with the examination of the bronze in sculptures discussed on pages 46 and 47, detailed computer analysis of the chemical elements contained in the clays from which pottery was made has become an effective means of classifying ceramic artifacts.

The technique for identifying the elements in clay is similar to the x-ray fluorescence process used on sculptures and paintings: A sample is bombarded with subatomic particles, and the effects are then measured to detect characteristic patterns. In addition to establishing differentiations between agora specimens *(below),* this method has been used to prove that pottery fragments found in widely scattered parts of the world—because their components are so nearly identical— must have come from the same source. The technique has thus helped confirm for historians the extensiveness of trade in the ancient world.

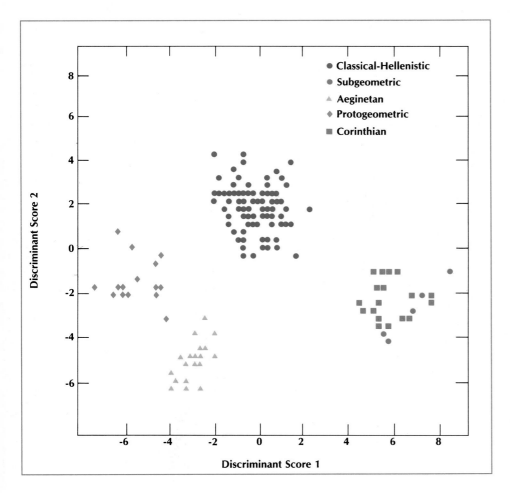

Statistical sorting. Once the chemical composition has been identified for an assortment of pottery fragments, a computer performs complex statistical tests such as discriminant analysis to rate their similarities and differences. As shown in the chart at left, five stylistic types of pottery found in the agora of Athens fell into four distinct compositional groups on the basis of their scores in two different tests, represented by the horizontal and vertical axes of the chart.

The Language Machine

When Ernest Hemingway published his novella *The Old Man and the Sea* in 1952, he was apparently seeking to disprove a widely held opinion that he had long since written himself out. High acclaim had greeted *The Sun Also Rises* in 1926 and *A Farewell to Arms* in 1929, but his work had not sustained his early promise, and his eminence had faded. Although critics praised *For Whom the Bell Tolls* in 1940, no memorable book followed it. Hemingway's reputation as a writer languished. *The Old Man and the Sea,* however, was greeted with critical accolades, publication in *Life,* and the Pulitzer Prize a year later; in 1954, Hemingway's lifework was crowned with the Nobel prize. While the novella was not considered superior to most of the author's prior works, it seemed to show that the old fire was still burning, that Hemingway's talent was as vital as it had been a quarter-century earlier.

But such a late return to earlier glory made at least one literary scholar suspicious. Perhaps the author had written the story much earlier, then pulled it out of a bottom drawer to demonstrate a capability that he in fact no longer possessed. The scholar was Darrel Mansell, an English professor at Dartmouth. Along with others, Mansell believed a writer's style to be an effect achieved almost unconsciously, arising from the way the entire personality arranges words into sentences while the conscious mind grapples with meaning. Further, he believed that a writing style evolves over time in ways that, while clearly detectable, are not consciously controllable, so that the writer cannot revert to an earlier mode of writing even if he wants to. Since *The Old Man and the Sea* struck Mansell as similar to work Hemingway had done around 1936, he was convinced that the author had written it some sixteen years before its publication. In 1970, Mansell mentioned his hypothesis to one of his students, a "computer jock" named William Koenig, who suggested that Dartmouth's campus computer might be able to help analyze the style and date the novella.

Professor and student worked out a statistical approach. By labeling and counting the nouns, verbs, and other parts of speech in pieces Hemingway wrote in different periods, Mansell hoped to produce "a kind of fingerprint of each writing sample that would differentiate it from the others."

Mansell earmarked for analysis 4,500 words of text from *The Old Man and the Sea.* He also selected four other 4,500-word samples of Hemingway's fiction, spanning eighteen years in the author's career, from 1933 to 1951. Mansell chose his samples not only for their dates but also for thematic similarity to *The Old Man and the Sea.* Like the novella, each dealt with a man engaged in a physical struggle—a submarine chase, a mock bullfight, a rum-running adventure, a reminiscence of war.

Mansell assigned students to tag every word in each sample with a three-digit code, one digit for its number of syllables (Hemingway uses no ten-syllable words) and the other two representing the word's grammatical part of speech. Every adjective, *(big, small, wet)* was labeled 10, every noun *(coffee, credit),* 50;

the main verbs were tagged 90, and the main verbs in dependent clauses, 95. Another label marked beginnings of sentences.

Koenig and another student, Brian Follett, programmed the computer to scan for and tabulate several measures of grammatical complexity. These included the number of words and syllables in each sentence, the number of words before the main verb in each sentence, and the ratio of descriptive words—adjectives and adverbs—to verbs in the sentences. They fed their tagged texts into the machine, and for each sample, the computer tallied a count for each measure. Once assembled, these counts formed a numerical portrait of each chunk of text, providing the "fingerprint" Mansell wanted.

After a computerized comparison of these statistical profiles, Mansell noted that *The Old Man and the Sea* resembled the earlier works much more closely than those written later. In particular, it had the most in common with the 1937 story, "The Capital of the World." Mansell concluded that the procedure had borne out his hunch about the novella's date of composition.

THE NUMBER CRUNCHER AS WORD CRUNCHER

Stylistic studies like Mansell's are only one application that literary scholars have found for computers over the past quarter-century. As soon as they discovered that these machines were not restricted to crunching numbers—that they would process all types of symbols, including alphabets and even the Egyptian picture writing called hieroglyphics—scholars began to use computers for a remarkably broad range of literary problems. The first application was in compiling a concordance, a reference catalog of the words used in a text, with the location and the surrounding context of each appearance of each word.

Scholars also recognized the advantages of having whole books and libraries in machine-readable form, and they set about creating electronic archives. The works recorded in such verbal data banks are available for simple lightning-fast

computer searches, as well as for increasingly sophisticated computer-assisted literary analyses. Dictionary making, based as it is on a fairly simple compilation process that is complicated by enormous scale, was another successful candidate for early computerization. Progress has been less steady in translation, the age-old, subtle process of converting statements in one language into statements in another. But the dream of computerized translation edges nearer as computers themselves aid in studies that chip away at one great obstacle: human ignorance about language.

JUST THE IMPORTANT WORDS, PLEASE

When the concordance was invented, toward the end of the thirteenth century, its first application was religious. Theologians were particularly concerned about the Scriptures' conflicting reports of the life of Jesus; if the Bible were divine truth, they reasoned, it ought to be consistent. At least, particular words that occurred in all four Gospels, they concluded, would indicate true historical events. Biblical scholars therefore determined to catalog the words, hoping to find the suspected "core of fact" beneath the variations. The resulting reference book listed each major word (*God, loved,* and *world,* but not function words such as *for, so,* or *the*) with every location (book, chapter, and verse) where it appeared, along with several surrounding words of context. Biblical concordances proliferated: They did not resolve the Gospels' inconsistencies, but they turned out to be very useful tools, not only for locating particular words but for suggesting topics for sermons. By the nineteenth century, the practice of analyzing texts through concordances had extended to literary works, including those of Shakespeare, Wordsworth, and Milton.

As compiled by hand, concordances required a tremendous commitment of time and energy. For each significant word in a work, a separate card first had to be made, bearing the word, its location, and often a whole sentence as the context. For example, the first sentence of the Bible, "In the beginning, God created the heaven and the earth," calls for five separate cards, each showing one major word (such as *beginning),* the citation (Genesis I, 1), and the entire sentence. It is easy to see why a completed "major-word" concordance would be seven to nine times as bulky as the original text.

Concording one long text, such as the Bible, could consume decades; James Strong's *Exhaustive Concordance of the Bible,* published in 1894, was thirty-five years in the making. Thus, when in 1908 Professor Lane Cooper of Cornell University set out to compile a concordance to the works of William Wordsworth, he recruited sixty-seven helpers to copy out citation slips for every significant word. The 211,000 handwritten slips still took seven months to produce; alphabetization was a separate chore. To have included the function words, which constitute about half of a work written in English, would have made such a project even more unwieldy and time-consuming.

But it was precisely this one glaring shortcoming of the standard concordance—its omission of the function words—that led to the first computer-assisted, automatized concordance. Father Roberto Busa, an Italian Jesuit priest, classics scholar, and philosophy professor, began his academic career in 1941 by studying, with the aid of word lists and subject indexes, the concept of "presence" in the works of Saint Thomas Aquinas. This concept would have

Creating a Concordance

A concordance is an alphabetized list of the words that appear in a written work or body of writings. Such lists are of interest to scholars analyzing the ways language is used or searching for particular phrases or ideas within lengthy passages of text. The ability of computers to organize massive amounts of data has turned the once-laborious chore of making concordances into a relatively straightforward matter. The key is software that is able to distribute data—words in this case—into a well-ordered structure in which individual words are easy to find and the total demands on computer memory are minimized.

A common software solution is a data structure called the binary tree. This method of organizing information takes its name from the way that data entered into the system forms a network of branches—never more than two from any point. Each new word produces a branch that defines an alphabetical relationship to all the other words on the tree. Subsequent searches for individual words are very efficient, though more so if the tree has grown in a balanced form with equal numbers of words to the left and right at each branch point. If the original ordering of the words has resulted in an uneven growth of the tree, the search times may be longer.

In addition to arranging words alphabetically, most concordances store other types of information. Often, a concordance counts how many times each of the words appears and has a system for remembering where the words came from.

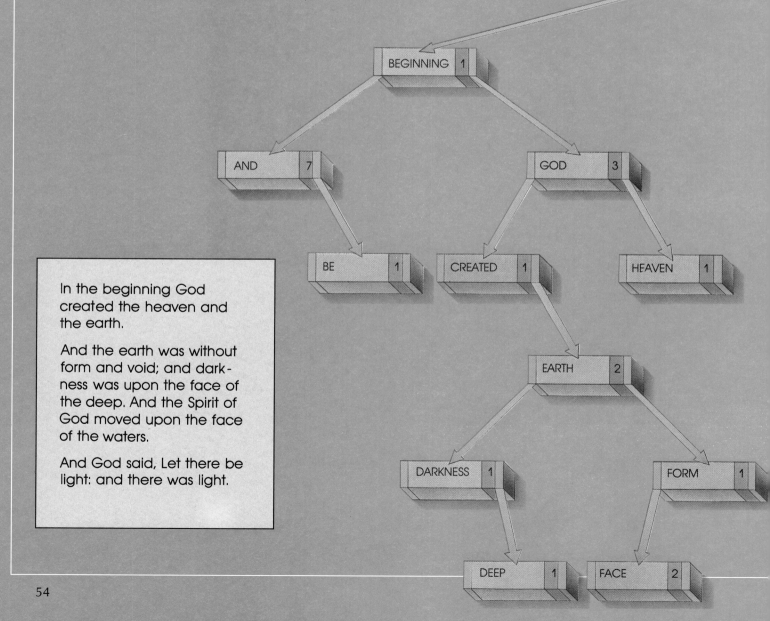

In the beginning God created the heaven and the earth.

And the earth was without form and void; and darkness was upon the face of the deep. And the Spirit of God moved upon the face of the waters.

And God said, Let there be light: and there was light.

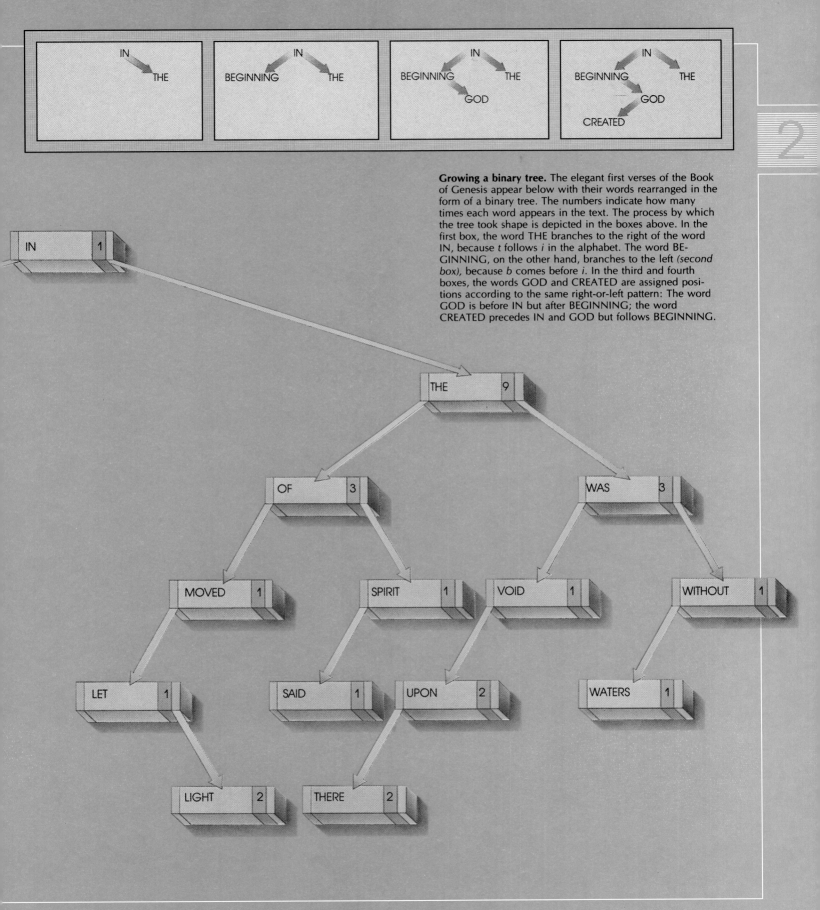

Growing a binary tree. The elegant first verses of the Book of Genesis appear below with their words rearranged in the form of a binary tree. The numbers indicate how many times each word appears in the text. The process by which the tree took shape is depicted in the boxes above. In the first box, the word THE branches to the right of the word IN, because *t* follows *i* in the alphabet. The word BEGINNING, on the other hand, branches to the left *(second box)*, because *b* comes before *i*. In the third and fourth boxes, the words GOD and CREATED are assigned positions according to the same right-or-left pattern: The word GOD is before IN but after BEGINNING; the word CREATED precedes IN and GOD but follows BEGINNING.

Creating a Concordance

Extracting the concordance. The product of the binary tree is an alphabetized list of words and numbers *(below)*. The steps the computer took to create this concordance are traced by the wavy lines on the diagram. Though the path of these lines appears random, the computer is following definite rules built into the concordance software. The object is to move through the tree from far left to far right, picking up the words in an order defined by their relative locations on the tree. The first step *(yellow)* is to find the widest branch to the left from the word IN, at the top of the tree. Temporarily bypassing the word BEGINNING, the computer comes to rest on AND, and puts that word on the list. In the second step *(orange)*, the computer searches for a branch to the right and finding BE, immediately looks for a path to the left. Finding none, it adds BE to the list and looks for a branch to the right. Stymied again, the computer retreats to the word BEGINNING and adds it to the list *(red)*. When there is no way to branch either left or right, the computer goes back to the last word passed over in the search. Bypassing GOD for the word CREATED *(purple)*, the process continues in the same fashion until every word has been plucked from the tree.

AND	7
BE	1
BEGINNING	1
CREATED	1
DARKNESS	1
DEEP	1
EARTH	2
FACE	2
FORM	1
GOD	3
HEAVEN	1
IN	1
LET	1
LIGHT	2
MOVED	1
OF	3
SAID	1
SPIRIT	1
THE	9
THERE	2
UPON	2
VOID	1
WAS	3
WATERS	1
WITHOUT	1

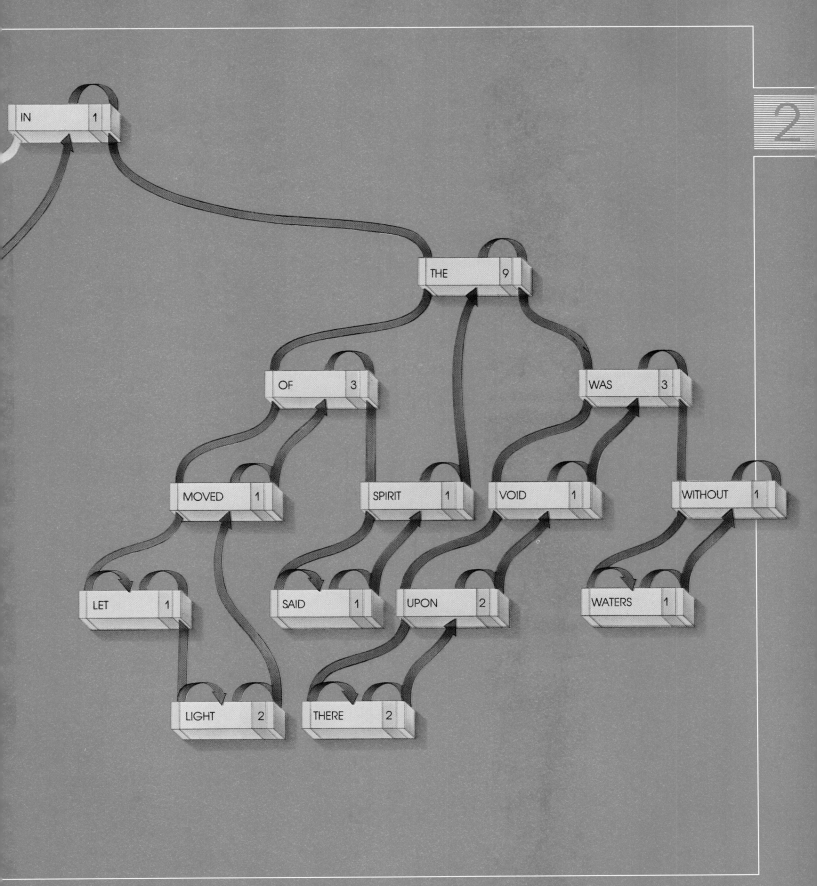

been easy to trace if the saint had used the Latin word *praesens* to express his thoughts. That noun, however, was absent from most of the texts. Aquinas had relied instead on the preposition *in,* writing, for example, "Reason in man is rather like God in the world." Thus a major theme of his doctrine could not be traced through standard concordances, because the word used to discuss it—*in*—was one of those deemed too insignificant to catalog. Four years' poring over texts, compiling his own 10,000-entry *in* list to track down the elusive teachings, convinced Busa that a truly complete concordance, function words and all, was needed for the works of Aquinas. The task would be formidable; the texts he wanted to process contained more than 10 million words, by his estimate. He began searching for a way to mechanize at least part of the labor.

In 1949, Busa's inquiries took him to the New York offices of IBM. Busa had

Standing beside the lectern of Milan's Santa Maria dei Miracoli church in August 1961, Father Roberto Busa reviews a printout of his computerized concordance, or word index, to the works of Saint Thomas Aquinas. The IBM 701 mainframe computer Busa used in this work was temporarily housed in the church during a move to more customary office quarters. The two robed monks assisted Busa by proofreading passages from Aquinas that had been entered into the computer.

sent details of his project ahead, and feared that the man he was to meet, company president Thomas J. Watson, Sr., would announce that the proposal was impossible. In the waiting room, Busa spotted a poster bearing an IBM slogan: "The difficult we do right away; the impossible takes a little longer." He put it in his briefcase and went into Watson's office. "Sitting in front of him," the priest later said, "and sensing the tremendous power of his mind, I was inspired to say, 'It is not right to say no before you have tried.' " Busa pulled out Watson's own slogan, and the executive agreed that IBM would help. Watson was true to his word. IBM supported his work, "even," Busa reported, "when it was not clear how long the project could take."

Watson appointed an adviser to help Busa apply IBM hardware to his project. Busa returned to his base near Milan, Italy, with a few IBM machines, including a couple of keypunch machines, for recording data as holes in cards from which IBM equipment received information, and card readers for processing the data. Busa began to have the texts keyed into punch cards, one line of text to a card; a machine then punched a new card for each word, with reference codes that indicated where the word could be found among Aquinas's writings.

Checking the cards for errors was a cumbersome process. Cards could not be read by the machine used to punch them but had to be fed through a tabulator-lister, which printed their contents on paper. When the printout was proofread and errors were found, entirely new replacement cards had to be punched—since a hole, once punched, could not be unpunched. Then the new cards were checked by the same process. Corrections took four times as long as punching the original cards.

Finally, in 1967, the last of Busa's texts was punched into cards. Over the next thirteen years he moved his project to Pisa, Italy, to Boulder, Colorado, and to Venice, Italy—wherever IBM could give him time on the computers for sorting, alphabetizing, and preparations for typesetting. Total computer time during Busa's thirty-year project was no less than 10,000 hours. Human work came to 1,800,000 hours, and by comparison the machine time may seem small, said Busa, but it represents the greatest possible automatization, and it speeded the sixty-volume, 70,000-page project phenomenally. "In twenty-five years," he explained, "we processed an average of 2,200 words per working hour, or four lines of text per minute."

TRANSFORMING CONCORDANCE MAKING

Commenting on his project, Busa remarked on a great distinction between the use of computers in linguistic analysis and in scientific computation. "The latter has comparatively little input, little output, huge processing," he said; "the former has huge input, huge output, comparatively little processing." During the course of Busa's work, the concording process changed completely; the nature and the uses of the input, the forms taken by the output, and the processing itself (pages 54-57) were all transformed in the intervening decades.

In 1957, eight years after Busa first met with Watson, the Reverend John W. Ellison, an Episcopal minister from Massachusetts, published the first truly computerized biblical concordance, produced with dazzling speed. Ellison began by having the entire Bible typed twice, onto separate magnetic tapes. To catch typing errors, he used a Remington Rand Univac to compare the two tapes, all but certain that the two versions would not contain identical mistakes. He fed the corrected master tapes back into the Univac, which he instructed to label every word according to book, chapter, and verse. Then the computer discarded the function words, added context to the words remaining, and alphabetized the entries. All these tasks were accomplished in only 400 hours' processing time.

Then in the mid-1960s Marvin Spevack, an American professor of English at Westfälische Wilhelms-Universität in Münster, West Germany, undertook a computer-generated concordance to William Shakespeare's plays. In nine volumes, the last of which was published in 1980, Spevack presented a separate concordance to each play, and even a concordance to the vocabulary of each character. Although the length of context he could supply for each entry was limited by the forty-eight spaces on his punch cards, Spevack vastly increased his work's usefulness by concording all of Shakespeare's 884,647 words—including the stage directions and function words, which earlier concorders had been forced to omit.

For Ellison's work, and for Spevack's and Busa's, the programming problems fell to computer experts, who were called in to write the needed software. By 1980, however, many ready-made programs were available for generating a concordance from a text on file with a computer. The best of these accomplish, on desktop personal computers, a job that once required a mainframe. Word-Cruncher, for example, a program written at Brigham Young University and formerly named the BYU Concordance Program, can concord an average-size novel in about ninety minutes.

ELECTRONIC LIBRARIES

So focused were early concorders on the final product that they tossed aside the original text, so painstakingly keyed into a computer. Hundreds of pounds of punch cards and miles of magnetic tape simply went into the trash. Eventually, however, scholars recognized this raw data as a valuable, infinitely manipulable database, and the electronic library was born. The first such library started in the 1970s when Oxford Computing Service in Oxford, England, began to provide shelter for any machine-readable texts scholars cared to donate. Expanded since then, the archive includes texts in twenty-eight languages, and it has created and distributed the Oxford Concordance Package, a program that generates concordances.

Most electronic libraries are less eclectic than Oxford Computing Service in the literature they collect. For example, the Thesaurus Linguae Graecae (Latin for "Treasury of the Greek Language"), at the Irvine campus of the University of California, contains literary relics of a single culture. Started in 1972 under the direction of Theodore F. Brunner, this compendium includes virtually every scrap of Greek that has survived from the Classical period. On file are more than 18,400 complete works and fragments, totaling more than 60 million words, from the epic poetry of Homer in the eighth century BC to the prose histories composed at the end of the sixth century AD. Even more massive is the Global Jewish Database/Responsa Project, one of the largest nonnumeric databases in the world. Residing in an IBM 3081 computer on the campus of Bar Ilan University near Tel Aviv, the GJD/RP is projected to contain all of the most important works of Jewish religion and culture: approximately 250 million words of text, or 1.4 gigabytes (1.4 billion bytes). Converting such records into databases permits scholars to search in mere minutes through the accumulated knowledge of many centuries.

WHO DONE IT?

Storing text in computer-readable form in order to search it for information is elementary compared to the use of computers to establish authorship of a literary work. The pioneering in this field, which led to Mansell's analysis of Hemingway's writings, was done in 1963 by two statisticians, Frederick Mosteller of Harvard University and David Wallace of the University of Chicago. At that time, the two men were collaborating on a method for solving problems that involve correctly assigning items to categories. Such assignments are easy to make when the items differ clearly, but when items share characteristics, pigeonholing them appropriately becomes chancier. Mosteller and Wallace's idea was that characteristics identified as strong in members of one category and weak in members of another could be analyzed statistically to make suitable classifications.

To test this theory, they chose a problem of classification that had eluded solution for 175 years. In 1787 and 1788, John Jay, Alexander Hamilton, and James Madison, three of America's founding fathers, published *The Federalist Papers*. These eighty-five essays, intended to persuade readers to ratify the newly proposed Constitution, were all printed under one pseudonym. Attribution of most of the essays was clear from historical information. However, for fifteen of them, Hamilton and Madison had made conflicting claims, and historians had labored in vain to produce convincing evidence that would resolve the case.

The two men's writings are not distinguishable at a glance; both had mastered a complex, oratorical style built of sentences averaging thirty-five words in length. But Mosteller and Wallace hoped that they could identify characteristics in the disputed essays that would establish once and for all whether Madison or Hamilton had written them. The computer's role was to take over the repetitious labor of examining a wide assortment of prospective discriminators, most of which turn out to have been used similarly by the two authors.

The two statisticians began counting and tabulating words. They created separate word indexes to each of the disputed papers, as well as to several essays known to have been written by Hamilton and to several by Madison. Each index listed all the words used in a given set of papers, along with the number of times each word was used. Part of this tabulation was done by a computer working with punch-card input, and part was done by hand.

Function words once again took center stage. "The best single discriminator we have ever discovered," they reported, "is *upon.*" Hamilton used it three times in every thousand words, while Madison used it only once in every six thousand. Another discriminator was *while,* the word Hamilton used, where Madison used *whilst.* Using such findings, the statisticians attributed the disputed essays to Madison, a conclusion accepted by students of history and literature alike.

A more elaborate stylistic analysis was brought to bear on an attribution dispute centering on *The Silent Don,* a masterpiece of Soviet literature and the most widely read novel in the Soviet Union. This four-volume work follows the members of a Cossack village from just before World War I through the 1917 Russian Revolution and the ensuing civil war. Mikhail Sholokhov, a novelist born in the Don River region, published the books beginning in 1928. From the first, *The Silent Don* was dogged by charges that Sholokhov had plagiarized it, stealing from Cossack author Fyodor Kryukov, who died in 1920.

To resolve the question, Geir Kjetsaa, a Norwegian authority on Slavic literature, in 1975 undertook a computer analysis of 3,000 sentences, one-third from works known to be Sholokhov's, one-third from Kryukov, and the final third from *The Silent Don*. Kjetsaa used eight criteria, including word-frequency measures like those used in the *Federalist* analyses. He also examined the sequence of nouns, verbs, and adjectives in sentences, an especially revealing matter of style in Russian, which allows great freedom of word order. With the results of all eight tests in agreement, Kjetsaa concluded that *The Silent Don* resembled Sholokhov's work more than it did Kryukov's.

In analyses like these, a computer scanning a written work—or even scanning all of an author's writings—easily discerns patterns that are imperceptible to the human reader. One such pattern is the frequency of new words; that is, in a given piece of writing, how many words occur that appear nowhere else in works by the same author? Unlikely as it may seem, the rate of new-word use varies widely from author to author and stays fairly constant from one work to another by the same author. This characteristic provides another literary fingerprint that can be used to distinguish between works by different authors.

In 1975, merely as a statistical exercise, Stanford University statistician Bradley Efron and one of his students, Ronald Thisted, performed a specialized statistical analysis of Shakespeare's works, to calculate the rate at which the poet introduced new words. Computers provided their raw data through Spevack's complete concordance to Shakespeare, which offered this information: Of the 884,647 words in all of Shakespeare's known works, 31,534 different words appear. Of these, 14,376 occur only once, 4,343 are used twice, 2,292 make three appearances—the calculations go on up to words that show up 100 times. Applying a rarefied theorem to these figures, Efron and Thisted gained remarkable insight into how Shakespeare freshened his English. In any work, they said, they could predict how many of the words Shakespeare had never used before, how many would appear one other time, and so on. But they never thought they might apply their discovery to a real Shakespearean puzzle.

In 1985, however, Efron and Thisted got their chance. Shakespearean scholar Gary Taylor, delving into seventeenth-century manuscripts in an Oxford University library, found an unpublished poem that he believed to be the work of Shakespeare. Other scholars disagreed, but when Efron and Thisted ran their analysis on the 430-word poem, the pattern kept "coming out beautifully," said Efron. As a control, the pair ran the same tests on selected works by three of Shakespeare's contemporaries. The patterns of word introduction of these writers were clearly not the bard's. Even so, Efron and Thisted cautiously reported, they had proved not that Shakespeare wrote the overlooked poem, but that there is no reason to reject the hypothesis that he did.

LOOK IT UP

The information-rich word list compiled in a concordance is but a token of the word-handling prowess of computers. Lexicography, the making of a dictionary, calls for some of the same capabilities. Obviously useful, dictionaries are a relatively recent invention. Not until the end of the fourteenth century, soon after concordances were invented, did academics recognize that an alphabetical list of words and their definitions might be worth compiling. Like the entries for a concordance, each entry for a dictionary had to be written on a separate slip of paper, then the myriad slips had to be alphabetized. When in 1857 the Philological Society of London set out to compile a dictionary of all the words ever used as part of the English language since the twelfth century, hundreds of volunteers, many of them learned clergymen, helped by sending citation slips—words, with illustrative quotations—to be used in selecting the word list. The resulting reference work, the monumental twelve-volume *Oxford English Dictionary (OED),* took more than seventy years to produce. No wonder, then, that in 1755 Samuel Johnson, in his *Dictionary of the English Language,* had defined a lexicographer as "a harmless drudge."

Dictionary makers turned early to computers for help with the drudgery. In the 1960s, both the *American Heritage Dictionary* and the *Random House Dictionary* were produced with computer assistance. Even the venerable *OED* has entered the computer age. Keeping the *Oxford English Dictionary* up-to-date has required the issue of five supplemental volumes between 1933 and 1986. Even so, supplements could not be prepared quickly enough to keep pace with the rapidly changing language. Moreover, the *OED,* now some 21,000 pages long, had grown cumbersome to use. To avoid complicating the *OED* with more addenda—and to begin using computer-driven typesetting methods—Oxford University Press, the publisher, determined in 1984 to convert the dictionary to a machine-readable database. Doing so would be a huge job. The *OED* contains more than 320,000 entries, more than two million quotations, and more than 600,000 cross references. Typing its sixty million words would require 500 million keystrokes. The advantages of the conversion, however, were irresistible. Once finished, it would simplify the tasks of merging the supplements into the original, and of revising, correcting, and updating the complete work, to be known as the *Oxford English Dictionary, second edition.* And while the dictionary would also be issued in print, the database would allow scholars to undertake new studies of the dictionary.

According to Edmund Weiner, coeditor of the work, "each distinct information category within the dictionary—pronunciation, part of speech, subject label, definition, quotation, date, author, and all the rest—will be made a separate, accessible element within the database," so that a researcher can compare words according to any or all of these categories and can obtain immediate responses to "questions which at best take years to answer using the printed dictionary." A scholar could study the way Hindu words infiltrated the English language after the British Empire expanded into India. Or a list of words might be compiled, not alphabetically, but in order of their first recorded use. And having the dictionary in electronic form will make it vastly easier for lexicographers to find and correct inconsistencies. For example, under the entry "outer space," a 1901 quotation from H. G. Wells is given as the earliest usage; but the phrase also appears under the "space" entry in a quotation dated twenty-two years earlier.

Besides serving as new tools for doing the same old work, computers have opened the way for new kinds of dictionaries. One of the most notable is the *Dictionary of American Regional English,* or *DARE,* the first attempt at a com-

Hunting for Uruguay. This simplified drawing shows how a computer would search through a hierarchy to find the word *Uruguay* in a database. Starting at the top level, the computer determines that the third keyword *(green)* is closest alphabetically to *Uruguay* without preceding it. A pointer guides the search to the next level, where only the rightmost node's keywords are searched. The second keyword is closest and points to a node at the next level, and so on until *Uruguay* is found. Blank spaces *(gray)* in the lowest level indicate room for additions to the database, and horizontal arrows denote connections between nodes that facilitate the revision of keywords and the generation of sequential listings of the items in the database.

Speeding the Search through a Database

Programmers have devised an array of strategies for ensuring speedy access to the information stored in databases. The simplest approach is a sequential search, in which the computer is instructed to compare a selected item with each item in the database, one after another, until a match is found. If the database is relatively small and can be perused quickly, this method is usually the most efficient because it requires little programming sophistication. But for large-scale databases containing hundreds of thousands or even millions of entries, shortcuts are a necessity.

The procedure illustrated here for searching an alphabetized list of words relies on a hierarchical organization similar to the binary-tree structure demonstrated on pages 54-57. The top level of the hierarchy consists of a single node containing three keywords extracted from the full database, dividing the database into thirds; if the full database contained 270,000 words, the first keyword would be the 90,000th word, the second the 180,000th, and the third the 270,000th. The second level comprises three nodes of three keywords apiece,

dividing the database into ninths. Each subsequent level further subdivides the database until, at the lowest level, the entire list is represented.

The secret to this system's efficiency is that the computer searches only one node at each level, comparing the target word with each of the node's keywords in turn to determine the first one it precedes or matches, then moving down to the next level's node associated with that keyword. By narrowing the search in this way, the computer rapidly homes in on the precise word sought, in this example eliminating two-thirds of the possible choices at each level. An actual database might have as many as twenty keywords per node, indexing up to 3,200,000 entries in only five levels.

At the lowest level of the hierarchy, each entry indicates a memory location where the desired information is stored. In the case of a textual database, that data may consist of document numbers where a particular word is found, as well as numbers indicating the location of the word within each document *(bottom right)*.

Uruguay

Document No.	Word No.
4	24, 387, 1,242
7	827, 1,455
12	5, 27, 93, 215, 293, 386, 595

prehensive lexicon of American regionalisms. When complete, sometime early in the twenty-first century, *DARE* is expected to fill five volumes of more than a thousand pages each. So informative a reference tool can be created only from an enormous wealth of information. *DARE* at the outset possessed a paper archive of published research in regional speech going back to 1889. This archive had yielded a file of citation slips, painstakingly annotated; and to this traditional slip file, the *DARE* project added an unmatched collection of recorded interviews conducted in every state.

Beginning in 1965, under the direction of Frederic G. Cassidy at the University of Wisconsin, fieldworkers armed with tape recorders interviewed "informants," one from each of about 1,000 communities throughout the fifty states. Each respondent answered 1,847 questions. A typical question was: "When people bring baked dishes, salads, and so forth to a meeting place and share them together, that's a ___ meal." Interviewees filled this gap with 131 different responses, including "potluck," "covered-dish," "picnic," and "dinner on the ground" among the most frequent, as well as "pitch-in," heard only in southern Indiana. With multiple answers from many of those queried, the interviews netted about 2.5 million responses, each one coded with the informant's sex, race, level of education, age, and type of community. Conducting all the interviews took five years; transferring the data to magnetic tape, which took another five years, was completed in 1975.

Computerizing their compilation of this research, though not without its snags, was well worth the effort, allowing dictionary editors to use the computer for things that would have been too time-consuming to attempt manually. For example, a map-making program showed in less than a minute the distribution of a word according not only to geography, but to any combination of the demographic characteristics recorded for each informant. The speed of this process permits an editor to quickly examine a word according to many criteria to better assess the limits of its use and even its future in the language. The map for *belly-girt,* a term for the strap that holds a saddle on a horse, might be dotted with *O*s (for old) and *M*s (for middle-aged). If so, the word is used primarily by older speakers and may be going out of style.

For Volume I, all editing was done by hand on typewritten manuscript. But beginning with Volume II, thanks to the rise of the inexpensive microcomputer, this work will be accomplished with modern word-processing software on a computer screen. "We are constantly finding ways to increase computer use," notes director Cassidy, "wherever it actually saves time, money, or human energy." So far, however, *DARE* has not been able to put its traditional slip file onto tape. Storing all the valuable layers of comment and correction on the slips remains prohibitively expensive.

MASTERING FOREIGN TONGUES
Computerized lists of words and their meanings like the new *OED* and the *DARE* are an important first step toward an elusive goal for computers—to translate one language into another. Of all the computer's linguistic pursuits, translation has been the most intractable. Yet the need for automated translation is pressing, not so much in the world of arts and letters as in international trade and diplomacy. These fields have so expanded that the volume of documents to be translated—

from agreements governing fishing rights to owner's manuals for cars—threatens to outstrip the abilities of human translators to keep pace. For example, the technical manuals required for operating and servicing a military tank would fill the vehicle to overflowing. When a foreign-aid program includes tanks, all those thousands of pages of instructions must be translated into another language.

The idea of computerized translation was first raised shortly after World War II. At that time, Warren Weaver, vice president of the Rockefeller Foundation, was looking to fund innovative, nonnumeric work with computers. In a letter dated March 4, 1947, he wrote to his friend Norbert Wiener, a pioneer in the mathematical theory of communication: "I have wondered if it were unthinkable to design a computer which would translate." Weaver had heard of the successful application of computers to code breaking during the war and asked whether "the problem of translation could conceivably be treated as a problem in cryptography." Wiener's response was crushing: "I frankly am afraid the boundaries of words in different languages are too vague and the emotional and international connotations are too extensive to make any quasi-mechanical translation scheme very hopeful." Though Wiener's pessimism would be widely echoed, Weaver's idea was better received by a few other scientists.

One of them was Andrew D. Booth, a British physicist and inventor who wanted to build a computer for analyzing crystals. With Weaver's encouragement—and money—Booth turned to automated translation. Within a year, he had built a small computer and, with his colleague Richard Richens, was able to run for Weaver a rudimentary "automatic-dictionary" program that translated French into English. Based as it was on a short word list and a simple grammatical analysis of the text, the program produced barely acceptable results; the English version was riddled with awkward codes, some of them standing for words not translated. Weaver was encouraged nonetheless, and in 1949 he sent a memo to 200 highly placed acquaintances, urging on them "the possibility that computers be used for translation." So successfully did Weaver state his case, outlining general strategies and long-term objectives, that he put machine translation (henceforth to be known as MT) on the scientific map.

A GATHERING OF MINDS

By 1952 there were enough scientists working on issues relating to machine translation that the Rockefeller Foundation sponsored a conference at M.I.T. Eighteen men participated. Among them were Booth, the sole British participant, and Leon E. Dostert, from the Institute of Languages and Linguistics at Georgetown University in Washington, D.C. Dostert already had considerable experience with translation. He had served as Dwight Eisenhower's French interpreter during World War II and, at the Nuremberg war-crimes trials of 1946, he had devised the system of simultaneous translation, widely used ever since. In addressing the conference, Dostert expressed doubt that MT had much to offer. But by the end of the four-day meeting, not only had Dostert been converted, but he issued a rallying call for "the early creation of a pilot machine proving to the world not only the possibility, but also the practicality, of MT."

In the following months, research teams at several American universities tackled the problem. Many of them built on Booth and Richens's automatic-dictionary approach, in which the computer was programmed to look up each

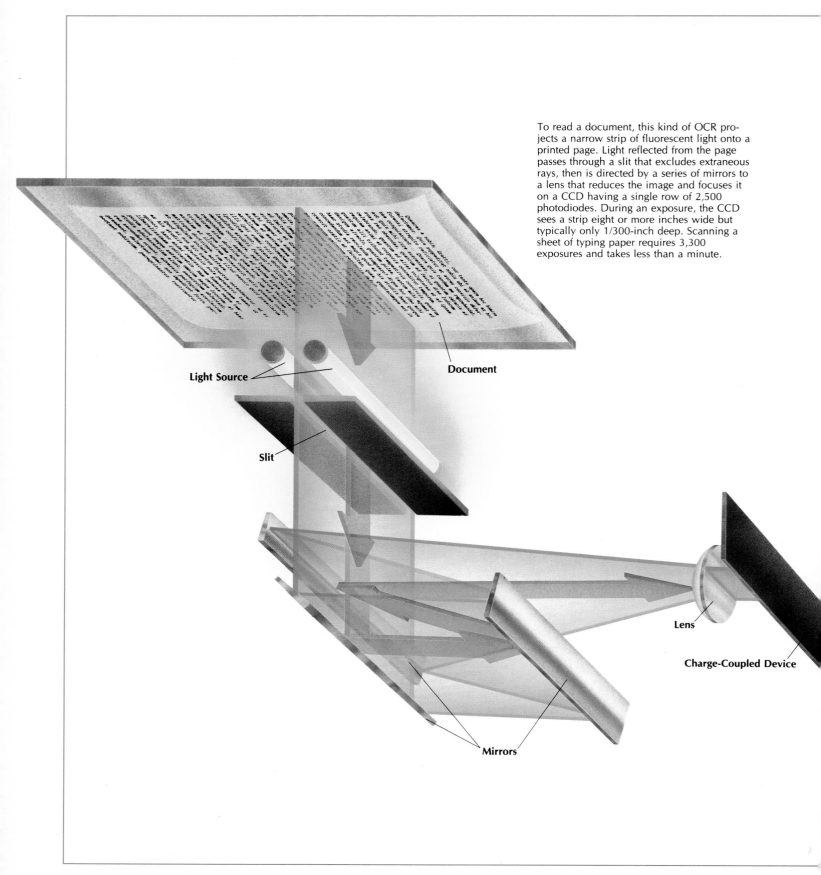

To read a document, this kind of OCR projects a narrow strip of fluorescent light onto a printed page. Light reflected from the page passes through a slit that excludes extraneous rays, then is directed by a series of mirrors to a lens that reduces the image and focuses it on a CCD having a single row of 2,500 photodiodes. During an exposure, the CCD sees a strip eight or more inches wide but typically only 1/300-inch deep. Scanning a sheet of typing paper requires 3,300 exposures and takes less than a minute.

Document

Light Source

Slit

Lens

Charge-Coupled Device

Mirrors

Reading the Printed Word

Transferring words from the printed page into computers can be a major obstacle in the way of using the machines for text research—to construct a concordance, to settle authorship, or even to search a document for specific information. For many years, the only solution was to retype the material, a time-consuming and costly undertaking. Optical character readers (OCRs) offer an alternative. These machines, which scan a document a page at a time, convert the shapes of letters into ASCII, the computer code widely understood by computers to represent letters, numbers, and punctuation.

Some OCRs scan by moving the page through the mechanism. Others read a page electronically, minimizing the number of moving parts in the device. The OCR shown at left scans the page with a moving beam of light, much as an office copying machine does.

But instead of reproducing the page on another piece of paper, an OCR projects a narrow strip of the text onto a charge-coupled device (CCD). This sensor consists of light-sensitive photodiodes on a chip. The photodiodes measure the light reflected from the document at each of millions of points. A computer converts low readings (from the dark shapes of letters) to ones and high readings to zeros. Then, using one of the schemes shown on the following pages, the computer identifies each letter.

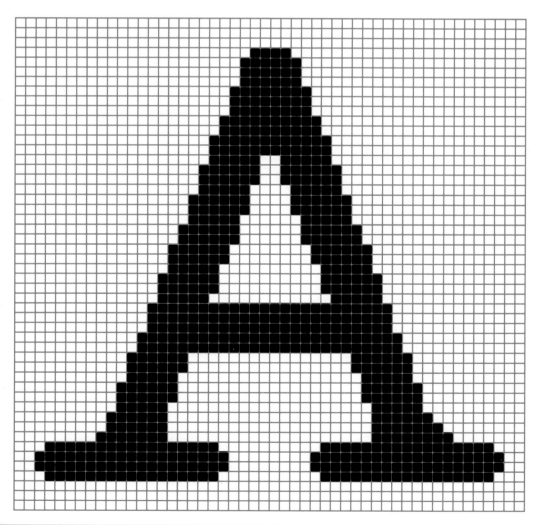

Each one of the squares in the diagram at left represents a pixel from an optical character reader capable of resolving 300 points per inch. Though the letter has zigzag edges, the shape is plain enough for a computer to recognize it as an *A*.

Point for Point, Feature for Feature

After a character has been scanned and digitized, the next step is to identify it. Two common methods, both of which compare the unidentified pattern to stored representations of letters, numbers, and punctuation, are explained here.

The simplest approach to character recognition is matrix matching *(below),* which relies on a stored matrix or template to represent the shape of each number, letter, and punctuation mark. Different sets of templates are stored for lowercase and capital letters, and for typefaces of different styles or sizes.

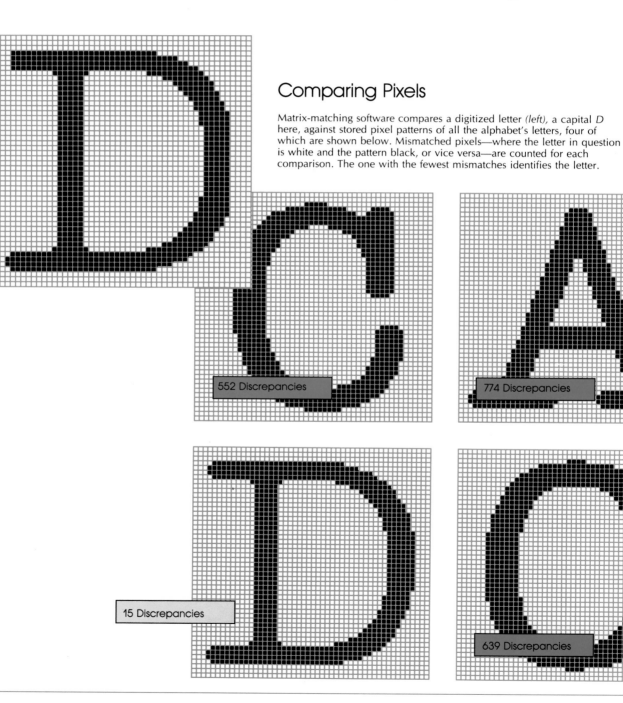

Comparing Pixels

Matrix-matching software compares a digitized letter *(left),* a capital *D* here, against stored pixel patterns of all the alphabet's letters, four of which are shown below. Mismatched pixels—where the letter in question is white and the pattern black, or vice versa—are counted for each comparison. The one with the fewest mismatches identifies the letter.

552 Discrepancies

774 Discrepancies

15 Discrepancies

639 Discrepancies

A close match between the unknown pattern and one of the templates allows both the letter and type style to be identified.

Matrix matching has limitations. It works only for typewriter fonts. Typewriter printing, unlike typeset print, accords the narrowest and widest letters the same amount of space in a line, thus making it possible to align templates and characters for comparison. Furthermore, such a system can recognize characters only from typewriter fonts that it has on file.

Feature analysis solves these problems. As shown below, this approach to character recognition compares the shapes or letters to stored descriptions rather than to digital snapshots of them. Because alignment with a template is unnecessary, feature analysis can handle the variable spacing between letters characteristic of typeset print. And because the basic shapes of characters change little for different typefaces and sizes, an OCR based on feature analysis needs a character-recognition library of only a few basic type styles, such as italic and regular type, and typefaces with serifs and without.

Comparing Features

Feature-oriented software typically examines an unidentified letter for basic characteristics: horizontal lines at the top, center, and bottom; diagonal lines slanting left or right; vertical lines on the left or right side; curves; line endings; and others. For each character, a list of features is compiled and is compared to similar lists on file for each letter (below).

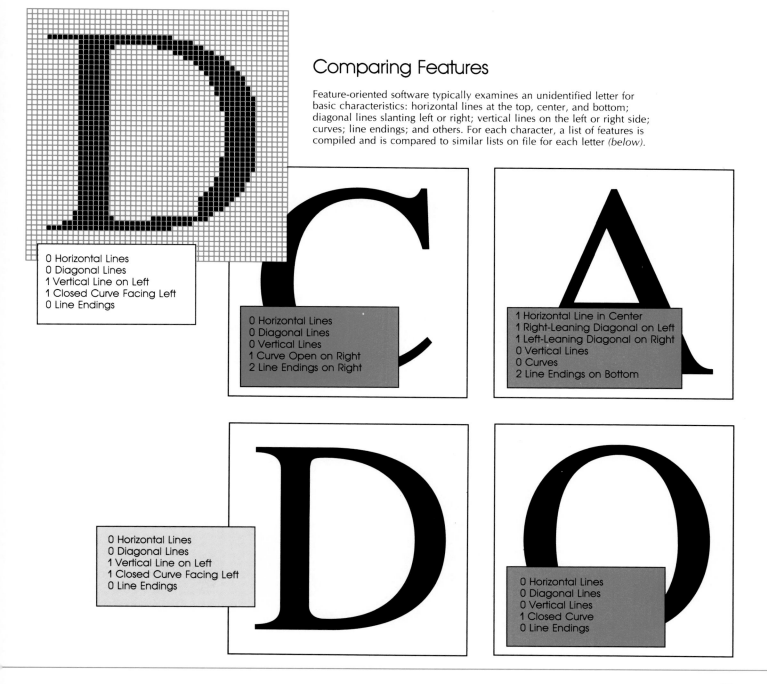

0 Horizontal Lines
0 Diagonal Lines
1 Vertical Line on Left
1 Closed Curve Facing Left
0 Line Endings

0 Horizontal Lines
0 Diagonal Lines
0 Vertical Lines
1 Curve Open on Right
2 Line Endings on Right

1 Horizontal Line in Center
1 Right-Leaning Diagonal on Left
1 Left-Leaning Diagonal on Right
0 Vertical Lines
0 Curves
2 Line Endings on Bottom

0 Horizontal Lines
0 Diagonal Lines
1 Vertical Line on Left
1 Closed Curve Facing Left
0 Line Endings

0 Horizontal Lines
0 Diagonal Lines
0 Vertical Lines
1 Closed Curve
0 Line Endings

Quam multas nobis imagines - non solum ad intuendem, verum etiam ad imitandum - fortissimorum virorum expressas scriptores et Graeci et Latini reliquerunt!

Quaeres a nobis, Gratti, cur tanto opere hoc homine delectemur. Quia suppeditat nobis ubi et animus ex hoc forensi strepitu reficiatur et aures convicio defessae conquiescant... Quare quis tandem me reprehendat, aut quis mihi iure suscenseat, si quantum ceteris ad suas res obeundas, quantum ad festos dies ludorum celebrando, quantum ad alias voluptates et ad ipsam requiem animi et corporis conceditur temporum, quantum alii tribuunt tempestivis conviviis, quantum denique alveolo, quantum pilae, tantum mihi egomet ad haec studia recolenda sumpsero? Atque hoc ideo mihi concedendum est magis quod ex his studiis haec quoque crescit oratio et facultas, quae, quantacumque est in me, numquam amicorum periculis defuit.

Pleni omnes sunt libri, plenae sapientium voces, plena exemplorum vetustas; quae iacerent in tenebris omnia, nisi litterarum lumen accederet. Quam multas nobis imagines - non solum ad intuendem, verum etiam ad imitandum - fortissimorum virorum expressas scriptores et Graeci et Latini reliquerunt! Quas ego mihi semper in administranda republica propenens animum et mentem meam ipsa cogitatione

hominum excellentium conformabam.

Quaeret quispiam, "Quid? illi ipsi summi viri quorum virtutes litteris iproditae sunt, istane doctrina quam tu effers laudibus eruditi fuerunt?" Difficile est hoc de omnibus confirmare, sed tamen est certum quid respondeam...: saepius ad laudem atque virtutem naturam sine doctrina quam sine natura valuisse doctrinam. Atque idem ego contendo, cum ad naturam eximiam et illustrem accesserit ratio quaedam conformatique doctrinae, tum illud nescio quid praeclarum ac singulare solere existere.

Quod si non hic tantus fructus ostenderetur, et si ex his studiis delectatio sola peteretur, tamen, ut opinor, hanc animi remissionem humanissimam ac liberalissimam iudicaretis. Nam ceterae neque temporum sunt neque aetatum omnium neque locorum; at haec studia adulescentiam alunt, senectutem oblectant, res secundas ornant, adversis perfugium ac solacium praebent, delectant domi, non impediunt foris, pernoctant nobiscum, peregrinantur, rusticantur.

Quaeres a nobis, Gratti, cur tanto opere hoc homine delectemur. Quia suppeditat nobis ubi et animus ex hoc forensi strepitu reficiatur et aures convicio defessae conquiescant... Quare quis tandem me reprehendat, aut quis mihi iure suscenseat, si quantum ceteris ad suas res obeundas, quantum ad festos dies ludorum celebrando, quantum ad alias voluptates et ad ipsam requiem animi et corporis conceditur temporum, quantum alii tribuunt tempestivis conviviis, quantum denique alveolo, quantum pilae, tantum mihi egomet ad haec studia recolenda sumpsero? Atque hoc ideo mihi concedendum est magis quod ex his studiis haec quoque crescit oratio et facultas, quae,

Optical character readers can distinguish between text, pictures, and smudges by looking for the distinctive and regular appearance of regularly spaced lines of type on a page. Areas missing this pattern are excluded from feature analysis. By means of complicated pattern-recognition software, some systems can even tell the difference between blemishes and pictures, saving the art and discarding the dirt.

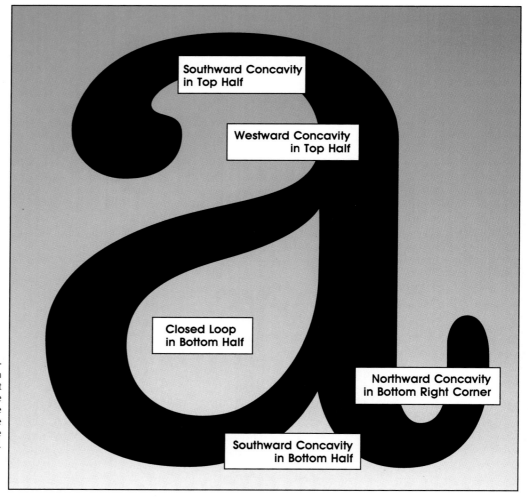

Southward Concavity in Top Half

Westward Concavity in Top Half

Closed Loop in Bottom Half

Northward Concavity in Bottom Right Corner

Southward Concavity in Bottom Half

Finely detailed descriptions of letters improve the accuracy of character recognition by feature analysis. In the lowercase *a* at right, for example, the curve at the top of the letter is subdivided into two curves, one facing down and one to the left. The concavities noted for the lower half of the letter help identify the *a*'s serif.

Finessing the Subtleties

Versatility and accuracy are conflicting goals in optical character reading. Matrix matching, though able to identify characters almost faultlessly, is fettered by its inability to handle typeset text. Feature analysis, while flexible, can be fooled by characters having identical descriptions, a capital *O* and a zero for example.

Most optical character-reading systems emphasize feature analysis and follow a variety of strategies to resolve the inevitable ambiguities. The zero and *O* can be distinguished by context-sensitive software that assumes a zero when the shape is flanked by other numbers. There are algorithms to distinguish words on a page from pictures *(left, top)*. Exquisitely precise descriptions of letters *(left, bottom)* help make recognition more reliable. Expert systems handle letters that run together, whether by accident or by intention *(below)*. A computerized dictionary can sometimes make sense of misidentified letters that spell a nonsense word.

If, after all this, the system errs, a human operator types a correct letter in place of a mistaken one, in effect teaching the system which character the questionable shape stands for. The next time the system comes across the letter, it has no trouble recognizing it.

Letters that touch each other, such as this *fi* from, say, the word *filling*, pose a complex problem for character-recognition systems. To identify the shape, the computer might first compare it to an internal list of letter combinations that often touch. Using rudimentary feature analysis, the computer narrows the list to a few candidates. For example, *wi* might be eliminated from consideration because the left side of the pair is too short to be confused with the letters in question. The combination *fl,* however, might remain in contention—but only until the computer consults its electronic dictionary. This test reveals no word beginning with the letters *flll,* so the computer correctly settles on *fi.* For cases that mystify the computer, the system operator must make the correction.

word in the source sentence and replace it with the equivalent word in the target language. Though it had been much improved since the original attempt in 1948, this word-for-word approach continued to cause difficulties. Because the computer had no means of distinguishing between homographs—words that are spelled the same but have different meanings—all possible interpretations of such words appeared in the translation. For example the word *bank* would have to be translated as "financial institution/edge of river."

The translations produced by this approach were clumsy, not only because of the multiple meanings that the human reader had to sort out, but also because of differences in word order between any two languages. Virtual nonsense like "Throw Grandpa down the stairs his slippers" was common. Nor could this word-for-word method handle phrases that are properly translated by single words. Thus the French *dans le même ordre d'idées* would be rendered as "in the same order of ideas" instead of "similarly." The Russian *po vidomomu,* which means "apparently," came out as "according to the visible."

While Booth and Richens's "automatic dictionary" was (and still is) essential for MT, it was quickly seen to be insufficient. Erwin Reifler, head of the Department of Far Eastern and Slavic Languages and Literature at the University of Washington in Seattle, proposed that humans assist the computer by preediting material to prepare it for translation and postediting the results. These operations would involve marking or revising the text before entering it into the computer, and then resolving the ambiguities and tidying up the style of the output. Reifler even suggested that scientists write their articles with the needs of MT in mind. Other researchers proposed that the preediting be done by the computer, which could code words according to function in a sentence, then rearrange them before translating.

The lesson taught by such experiments was that human languages are too complex and multilayered to be translated by any simple method. More sophisticated analysis was needed to examine not only the meanings of words but how they work with their neighbors as well.

A GOLDEN AGE OF MACHINE TRANSLATION

Dostert, meanwhile, took up the gauntlet that he had thrown down at the M.I.T. conference. At Georgetown University, he headed a small team composed of linguist Paul Garvin and two computer specialists from IBM. By January of 1954, just eighteen months after beginning work, the team had readied a public demonstration of MT. At IBM's Technical Computing Bureau in New York, running their program on the then-state-of-the-art IBM 701, Dostert's group showed the computer in action translating into English forty-nine simple Russian sentences about chemistry. Although the team's program had a limited vocabulary—just 250 words—it went beyond word-for-word translation. It was equipped by Garvin with six rules governing word order and choices between words with different meanings. Surprisingly graceful sentences resulted, informing observers, for instance, that "Starch is produced by mechanical methods from potatoes."

The demonstration proved, said Dostert, that genuine machine translation was possible, and that with adequate programming, preediting and postediting were unnecessary. Many more unbelievers were converted, and a new wave of optimism brought a tide of funding, largely from the military and military-intelligence communities. In the ten years that followed, nearly $20 million went into machine-translation studies carried on at seventeen institutions.

A FRONTAL ATTACK

The largest American MT project, funded by the Central Intelligence Agency through the National Science Foundation, was Dostert's at Georgetown. The line of attack pursued there—and widely adopted elsewhere—was known as the direct, or brute-force, approach. In this method, a programmer began by writing software to handle a particular text. The program included dictionary data for the passage, as well as the information needed to handle linguistic features of the text—how to distinguish a particular pair of homographs, for example. The machine would make several passes through each sentence, testing each time for a different linguistic feature. Then the programmer would amend the translation software, adding information and steps needed to prevent recurrence of errors the machine had made on the preceding text. Then the same program was used to translate another text and amended accordingly. The resulting software, though increasingly adept at translating Russian, was an inelegant, rather haphazardly constructed edifice.

Dostert's approach yielded a program called Georgetown Automatic Translation, or GAT. In June 1959, GAT translated 100,000 words of Russian on the subject of organic chemistry. The results were evaluated by an independent chemist at the university, who declared that "although their style was clumsy and the reading of them was time-consuming, the texts conveyed the essential information," a welcome development. The scientific community was feeling an urgent need for greater translation capacity. A recent UNESCO report had noted that at least half the scientific literature in the world was being written in languages that more than half of the world's scientists could not read. In this light, machine translations, though clumsy, were well worth having—and using.

Oak Ridge National Laboratory, a research facility of the U.S. Atomic Energy Commission at Oak Ridge, Tennessee, agreed to field-test the program on its powerful IBM 360 computer. François Kertesz, a Hungarian-born chemist and translator at the laboratory, ran the program at night and on weekends, processing Russian documents about nuclear physics. It was quickly obvious, said Kertesz, that the system was invaluable for screening scientific publications, allowing a physicist to decide whether a paper warranted full, formal translation.

The installation of the GAT program at Oak Ridge, where it went on serving for many years, was the crowning achievement of Dostert's team. But the event came as an anticlimax, following by a year the termination of the Georgetown MT project. Its major sponsor, the CIA, had unexpectedly withdrawn financial support, citing its disappointment with the quality of the translations. Yet abandonment by the CIA, though daunting, would prove to be only a foretaste of a money drought about to hit the entire American machine-translation enterprise.

A BLOW TO THE BODY

By 1964, the work that had begun amid a flurry of optimistic predictions a decade earlier seemed mired in difficulties all over the world, and one MT researcher wrote that the endeavor had "come up against the semantic barrier." Computerized translations would not be adequate, he said, until "the machine can 'understand' what it is translating and this will be a very difficult task indeed." This bleak view took hold among American sponsors of the research. The National Academy of Sciences formed a committee of scientists—the Automatic Language Processing Advisory Committee, known as ALPAC—to advise backers such as the National Science Foundation, the Department of Defense, and the CIA how to spend their research budgets. Of the committee's seven members, only two were MT specialists, and they, having become disillusioned about machine translation, had moved into other areas of work.

The ALPAC report was devastating. Holding the MT research community up to its own brash predictions, the ALPAC pronounced MT research a failure. In particular, the report noted that "when, after eight years of work, the Georgetown University MT project tried to produce useful output in 1962, they had to resort to postediting"; that is, correction by a human translator. While unedited machine output was "decipherable for the most part," said the report, "it is sometimes misleading and sometimes wrong, and it makes slow and painful reading." In view of the semantic barrier, ALPAC saw "no immediate or predictable prospect of useful machine translation," and recommended that funding of MT research be sharply curtailed.

Researchers in machine translation condemned the report as hostile, biased, and premature. Doing without postediting, they said, was an unreasonable goal; most translations rendered by humans also are spruced up by human editors. But wrongheaded or not, the committee had done its damage. The number of MT research centers in the United States shrank from ten in 1963 to just three in 1968. The report's dampening effect reached even the British, Japanese, and Soviet machine-translation projects.

SON OF GAT

Down but not out, MT survived—and even prospered. In California, a former Georgetown researcher and multilingual Hungarian named Peter Toma set up a company to develop his own GAT-based system for commercial uses. Called SYSTRAN, Toma's system improved on GAT in the structure of its programming. In GAT, an immense accumulation of instructions added up to a monolithic program in which the two steps of analyzing source-language sentences and synthesizing target-language sentences were not clearly separated. SYSTRAN makes these operations largely independent, so that alterations made in one do not affect the other.

In 1969 Toma sold his Russian-to-English SYSTRAN to the Air Force's Foreign Technology Division at Wright Patterson Air Force Base in Ohio. With additional programming for a second language pair, English-to-Russian, a SYSTRAN system was used in the Apollo-Soyuz Soviet-American joint space mission of 1974 and

1975. Then in 1976, the translation service of the Commission of the European Communities adopted SYSTRAN, and within three years was operating with three language pairs, English-French, French-English, and English-Italian.

Several other MT systems were up and running during the 1970s. The Moscow Patent Office used a computer to translate recently issued American patents into Russian. An American company called Logos Development Corporation developed a program for translating American military technical manuals into Vietnamese. In Quebec, the French-speaking province of Canada, a specialized program called TAUM-METEO, with a dictionary of only 1,500 items, began in 1977 to translate government weather reports from English into French at the rate of about five million words a year.

SYSTRAN, however, emerged as the largest and most productive machine-translation program in the world. After nearly twenty years of continuous refinement, the SYSTRAN Russian-to-English program, for example, grew to 300,000 terms and 200,000 idiomatic expressions. In its U.S. Air Force work alone, the program was translating more than 100,000 pages of Russian texts each year. And the SYSTRAN repertoire of language pairs had grown to nineteen.

THE WAVE OF THE FUTURE

Although SYSTRAN boasts many improvements over its ancestor GAT, it remains cumbersome. Each source-language analysis program is tailored to one target language. Expanding SYSTRAN to process additional language pairs requires starting almost from scratch with massive amounts of new programming, an expensive proposition for more than a couple of language pairs. The Commission of the European Communities, for example, needed the capability to translate seven languages. The agency recognized that expanding SYSTRAN to translate documents in all seven of these languages into each of the other six would require programming for forty-two language pairs. In 1976 the commission launched EUROTRA, a multinational MT research-and-development project to find a better way. Inspiration for this better way came from Warren Weaver's 1949 memo.

The "most promising approach of all," Weaver wrote, would be to seek "the common base of human communication—the real but as yet undiscovered universal language." EUROTRA's mandate was to translate text, not directly into another language, but into a string of codes containing all the information— semantic, syntactic, and grammatical—of the original. These codes could then be translated into any other language. In a seven-language community, an interlingual MT system of this kind would need, not forty-two language-pair programs, but only fourteen translation programs—seven for encoding, and seven to convert code to natural language. EUROTRA's efforts are expected to bear fruit sometime in the 1990s.

In the meantime, the demand expressed in the ALPAC report—for machine translations as graceful as natural human language—seems impractical, unrealistic, and in any case unnecessary. Machine translations continue to be used by scientists, military and intelligence experts, diplomats, businesses, and translation services in many parts of the world. The greater part of the machine output, while it is not polished prose, receives no subsequent human editing before serving as a useful step across language barriers.

Networks of Knowledge

Human knowledge doubles every eight years or so, a rate of growth that is both a blessing and a burden. As this body of information expands, finding desired pieces of data within it becomes more difficult. Computers help by speedily searching through the information. Yet such information, like that in libraries and encyclopedias, is typically organized to be retrieved in linear fashion—that is, in a set sequence.

"The human mind does not work that way. It operates by association," wrote computer pioneer Vannevar Bush in a prescient article in 1945. "With one item in its grasp, it snaps instantly to the next that is suggested by the association of thoughts, in accordance with some intricate web of trails

With a hypermedia system, the masses of information contained in a library of books, pictures, videotapes, and even ancient scrolls become easily accessible. Items can be quickly called into view not only by title or index number but also by their relationship to another item already on display.

carried by the cells of the brain." Bush suggested a desk-size machine that would operate like the human mind, connecting data according to relationships established by the user. Though Bush's visionary machine was never built, today software systems called hypermedia achieve his goal.

Hypermedia draws upon a store of information divided into blocks, called nodes, that contain text, graphics, sound, and video. A network of links connects the nodes; each node can be accessed through windows on the computer screen. Such an arrangement allows a user to pursue ideas in either linear or nonlinear fashion, jumping between nodes as associations leap to mind, or following trails of inquiry blazed by others.

One simple application of hypermedia may help home-buyers in a real-estate office. A computer displays a town map; then, at the click of a mouse, it zooms in on a chosen neighborhood. Additional clicks summon homes for sale, schools, shopping centers, bus stops, or even houses boasting special features such as pools or decks. A final click brings up pictures and descriptions of suitable properties.

Other versions of hypermedia offer an electronic encyclopedia, a catalog of automobile parts, and—as shown on the following pages—research in literature and art. The potential applications of hypermedia are as infinite as human thought itself—and no less supple.

A Versatile Cast of Nodes

The building blocks of a hypermedia system are its nodes, each in effect a chunk of information that represents a coherent concept. Portrayed here and on the following pages as shaded cubes, the nodes may contain information on virtually any topic and in any medium.

A node may comprise only a single word or picture, or it may contain an entire encyclopedia or film library. In practice, either extreme can be cumbersome. When no more than a sentence or two occupies each node, for example, the large

A general-purpose node *(left)* is one that places no restrictions on the organization or amount of information it contains. It can be used to hold anything at all, from an entire book to a brief paragraph or a color image.

A typed node, like the one at right, segregates information according to some classification scheme. One typed node might hold only graphics, another text. Or the typed node might contain details, commentary, or a central idea. In most systems, each class of typed node is assigned a distinctive color or icon so that the user can distinguish between classes with a quick glance.

number of nodes slows the system's operation. And when each of a small number of nodes contains an enormous volume of data, finding information within any single node becomes a daunting task.

The ideal size for a node depends on the information it holds. A sonnet or a painting, complete in itself, generally would be assigned to a single node. A work such as a novel or an aircraft-maintenance manual might reasonably be split up into several nodes, with one chapter or section in each node. But to realize Vannevar Bush's dream of search by association, the novel might also be divided into nodes containing references to a character, a locale, or an idea. And the maintenance manual could have nodes of parts-drawings or troubleshooting tips.

Such versatility calls for several kinds of nodes. Three common ones—a general-purpose node, a typed node, and a composite node—are described below, but any hypermedia system may also employ its own special-purpose nodes.

A composite node, made up of a group of individual nodes, is the best way to store pieces of information that share a common theme. This structure brings together a number of separate nodes under the umbrella of a single node, helping to thin the thicket of nodes confronting users. The composite node at left, for example, incorporates a collection of poems exploring a single thematic vision.

Through Windows to Information

To gain access to the information in a node, the hypermedia user presses keys or clicks a mouse to bring the node's contents onto the computer screen in a window. A window may be thought of as simply an open node—that is, a node on display. There are as many potential windows as there are nodes, and the system can display any number of windows on the screen at the same time.

The material in many windows includes labels or icons alerting the hypermedia user to the existence of links to re-

The window at right displays commentary on William Blake's poetry taken from a general node that is represented by a book. This selection discusses the contrast between the radiantly hopeful collection entitled *Songs of Innocence* and the darkly despairing *Songs of Experience*. Displayed simultaneously on the screen are two other windows, which bring into view examples from each collection: The examples are a celebration of infant joy, "The Lamb" *(below)*, and an ode to savage beauty, "The Tyger" *(opposite page)*.

Innocence versus Experience

Meanwhile there was nothing to do but record the truth as he felt it. That he once had found intense happiness was true; that he now found the exact reverse was equally true. He was too honest to close his eyes sentimentally upon the facts.

Therefore, in contrast to many of the *Songs of Innocence* he wrote antitheses. Against *The Lamb* stands *The Tyger*; against one *Nurse's Song* there is another; *Infant Joy* is offset by *Infant Sorrow*; and so on. It is rare to find any one with such courage of despair; rarer yet when such people do not allow the pessimistic present to cancel the happy past. Blake was certainly not trying to reverse the lesson he had so beautifully taught; instead he retained them both, carefully labelling them, to prevent misconstruction, 'the Two Contrary States of the Human Soul.'

The child knew no problems, and hardly felt suffering. The man sees problems everywhere, which he cannot solve. For this very reason (and this reason alone, as far as I can discover), the *Songs of*

The Lamb

Little Lamb who made thee
Dost thou know who made thee
Gave thee life & bid thee feed.
By the stream & o'er the mead;
Gave thee clothing of delight,
Softest clothing wooly bright;
Gave thee such a tender voice,
Making all the vales rejoice!
Little Lamb who made thee
Dost thou know who made thee

Little Lamb I'll tell thee,
Little Lamb I'll tell thee!
He is called by thy name,
For he calls himself a Lamb:
He is meek & he is mild,
He became a little child:
I a child & thou a lamb,

lated nodes; a few keystrokes, or a mouse click on an icon, instantly opens a new window on the screen. A window can be resized and repositioned; it can be erased or temporarily closed while leaving its icon present on the screen for easy recall. Position, size, and color help users to remember a window's contents.

Three windows are illustrated below, in drawings that represent a theoretical hypermedia system similar to one that is in operation at Brown University. The example traces an analysis of the works of the British poet-artist-mystic William Blake (1757-1827).

For this part of the study, the user has opened windows on poems taken from two collections in which Blake presents opposing views of the world. One poem, "The Lamb," from *Songs of Innocence*, is naive and joyful. Its antithesis, "The Tyger," from *Songs of Experience*, is disillusioned and bitter. A third window provides commentary and background to assist in the analysis.

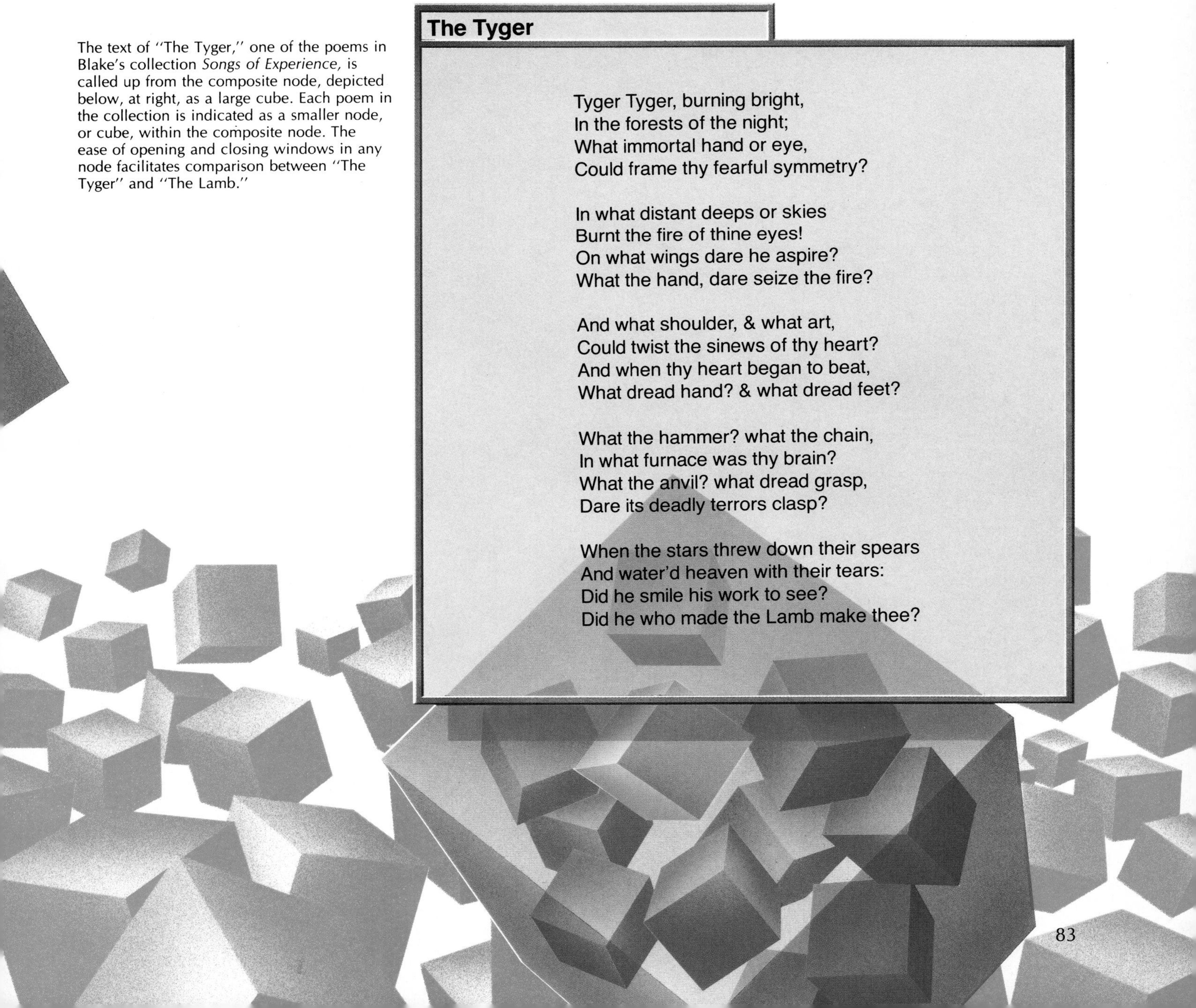

The text of "The Tyger," one of the poems in Blake's collection *Songs of Experience*, is called up from the composite node, depicted below, at right, as a large cube. Each poem in the collection is indicated as a smaller node, or cube, within the composite node. The ease of opening and closing windows in any node facilitates comparison between "The Tyger" and "The Lamb."

The Tyger

Tyger Tyger, burning bright,
In the forests of the night;
What immortal hand or eye,
Could frame thy fearful symmetry?

In what distant deeps or skies
Burnt the fire of thine eyes!
On what wings dare he aspire?
What the hand, dare seize the fire?

And what shoulder, & what art,
Could twist the sinews of thy heart?
And when thy heart began to beat,
What dread hand? & what dread feet?

What the hammer? what the chain,
In what furnace was thy brain?
What the anvil? what dread grasp,
Dare its deadly terrors clasp?

When the stars threw down their spears
And water'd heaven with their tears:
Did he smile his work to see?
Did he who made the Lamb make thee?

Links to Connect Diverse Ideas

The power of a hypermedia system to stimulate creative thinking stems from a network of links that guide users from one node to another. Links have several forms and functions. Some present annotations for topics related to a text or image; others indicate organizational structure among nodes. Links may connect a piece of text with successive sections, or they may join entries in a table or figure. In the example below, links originating from a phrase used by William Blake in *The*

A section of Blake's *The Marriage of Heaven and Hell* is displayed in the window at left. The phrase "corroding fires" is highlighted *(yellow)*, indicating the presence of a link. When the link is followed, it leads to a node holding an explanation much like a footnote, which reveals that "corroding fires" is an allusion to Blake's printing technique, which used acid to etch a relief on a copper plate. The second node also signals the presence of yet another link, this one leading to Blake's hand-colored print of his mythical deity Urizen measuring out the material world.

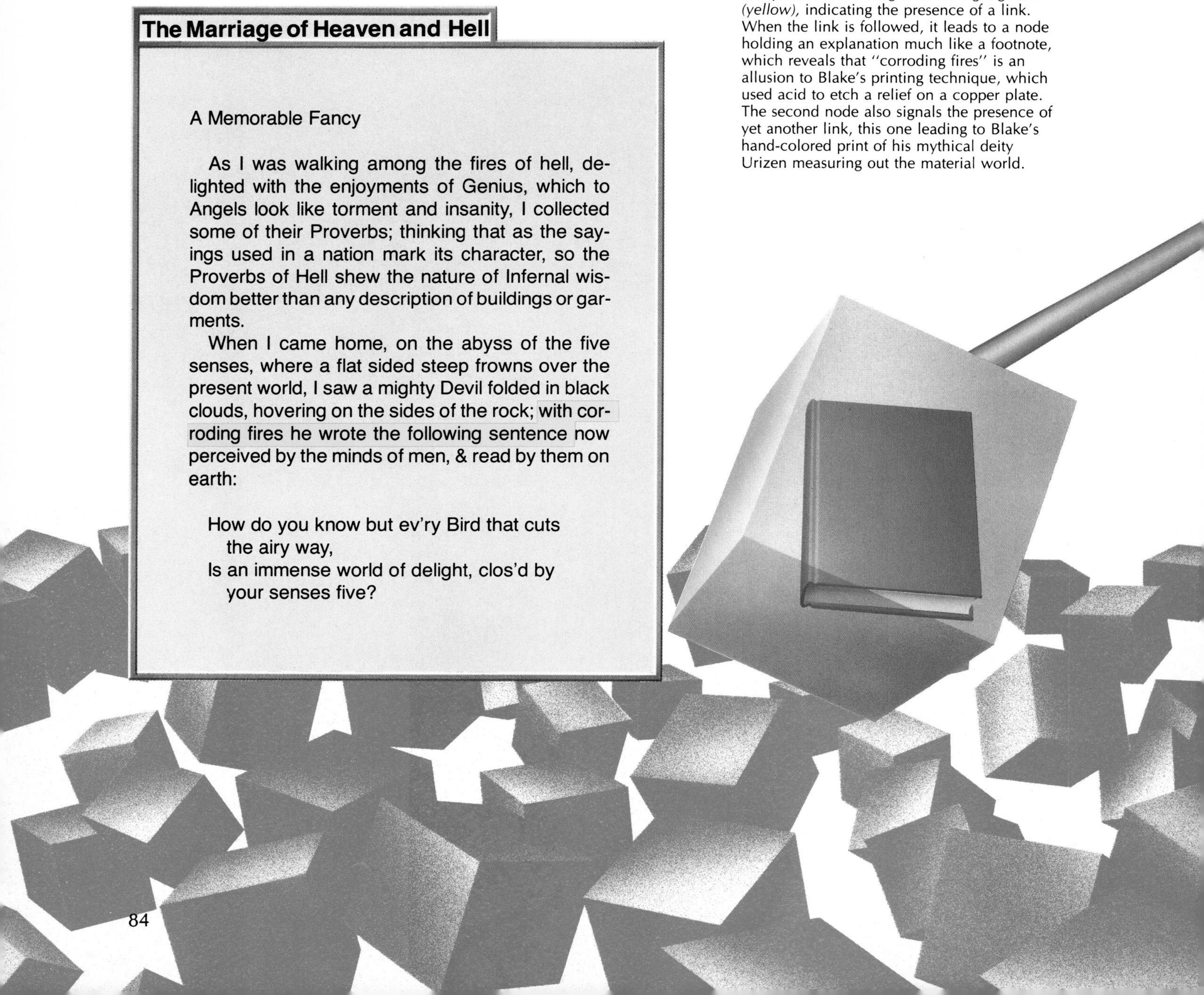

The Marriage of Heaven and Hell

A Memorable Fancy

As I was walking among the fires of hell, delighted with the enjoyments of Genius, which to Angels look like torment and insanity, I collected some of their Proverbs; thinking that as the sayings used in a nation mark its character, so the Proverbs of Hell shew the nature of Infernal wisdom better than any description of buildings or garments.

When I came home, on the abyss of the five senses, where a flat sided steep frowns over the present world, I saw a mighty Devil folded in black clouds, hovering on the sides of the rock; with corroding fires he wrote the following sentence now perceived by the minds of men, & read by them on earth:

How do you know but ev'ry Bird that cuts
   the airy way,
Is an immense world of delight, clos'd by
   your senses five?

Marriage of Heaven and Hell lead to an understanding of the relationship between Blake's poetry and his art.

Although the architect of a hypermedia system establishes many links in the process of designing the system, users may delete, rename, or forge their own links in a process similar to the copy-and-paste functions of word-processing systems. To change links, a researcher using the system indicates source and destination nodes, then chooses one of a variety of link commands. In cases where many links emanate from a source node, the links may bear explanatory labels designed to help the researcher navigate smoothly through the network of nodes.

As a general rule, the computer running the hypermedia system must be powerful enough to follow the links quickly, leaping back and forth between nodes with only the briefest delay—no more than a second or two.

Blake's printing techniques

In *Songs of Innocence* (1789) Blake inaugurated the method of publication he used for all his later original works, a procedure he had partly invented. He drew text and illustrations as a total pictorial design with an acid-proof substance directly on the copper plate, then applied acid so that the design was left in relief. With this plate he printed a page, which he later colored with watercolors by hand and bound with the other pages to make up a volume. The procedure of making the plates was

Europe, a Prophecy frontispiece

Different Links for Different Purposes

The simplest scheme for linking nodes of information organizes the material the way a traditional outline does: A "parent" node, containing the most general overview, is divided by some classification system into "child" nodes, each of which can be further subdivided into a hierarchy. These repeatedly branching links—illustrated below—can be pursued in any direction: up, down, or sideways. At any node, the user can jump to a parent, sibling, or child node, following links to information that is more general or more specialized,

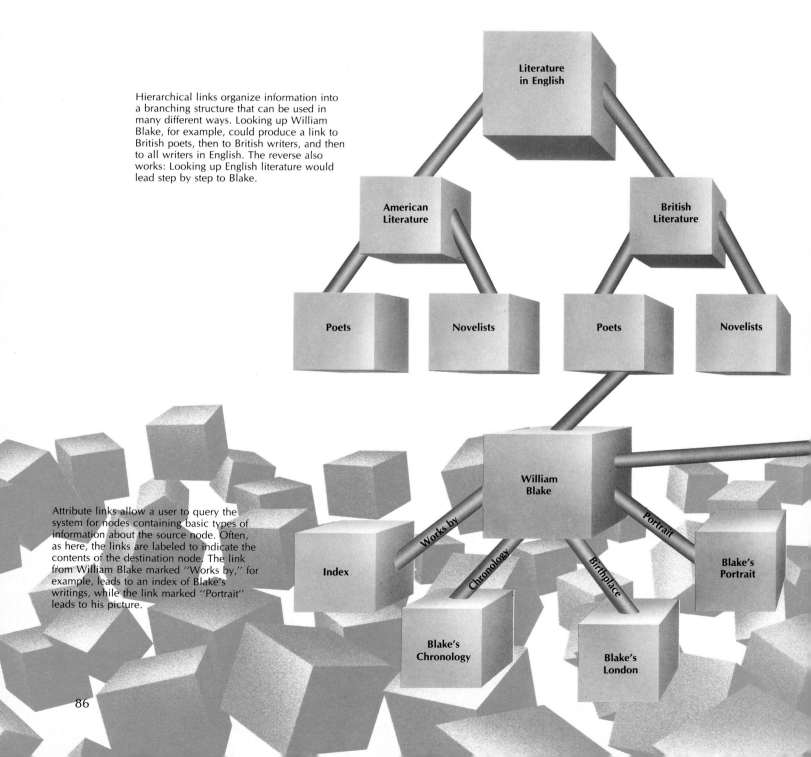

Hierarchical links organize information into a branching structure that can be used in many different ways. Looking up William Blake, for example, could produce a link to British poets, then to British writers, and then to all writers in English. The reverse also works: Looking up English literature would lead step by step to Blake.

Attribute links allow a user to query the system for nodes containing basic types of information about the source node. Often, as here, the links are labeled to indicate the contents of the destination node. The link from William Blake marked "Works by," for example, leads to an index of Blake's writings, while the link marked "Portrait" leads to his picture.

or to other information that is related only in a broad sense.

The disadvantage of hierarchical links lies in their need for rigid classification systems—ones that would naturally come to mind when the user is searching for the information needed. That requirement is difficult. A comparison of land- and sea-based life-forms, for instance, cannot be undertaken easily in a hierarchy that begins by distinguishing between plant and animal life.

To provide greater flexibility in searching—and to bring hypermedia closer to Vannevar Bush's ideal of a machine that represents information conveniently to the human mind—a number of different types of links have been developed. All have source and destination nodes; in some, a single link interconnects several nodes. Most links can be traversed in either direction. But in one type *(bottom left),* the destinations are attributes of the source, while in another *(bottom right)* they consist of widely diverse material that is related to the source only by association.

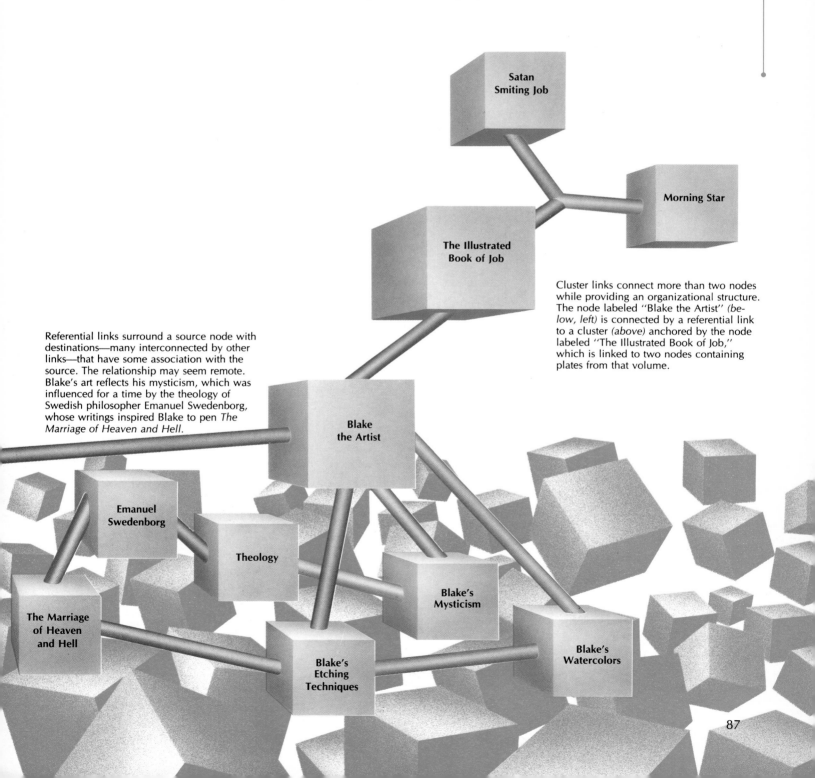

Cluster links connect more than two nodes while providing an organizational structure. The node labeled ''Blake the Artist'' *(below, left)* is connected by a referential link to a cluster *(above)* anchored by the node labeled ''The Illustrated Book of Job,'' which is linked to two nodes containing plates from that volume.

Referential links surround a source node with destinations—many interconnected by other links—that have some association with the source. The relationship may seem remote. Blake's art reflects his mysticism, which was influenced for a time by the theology of Swedish philosopher Emanuel Swedenborg, whose writings inspired Blake to pen *The Marriage of Heaven and Hell.*

87

Browsing: British Poets

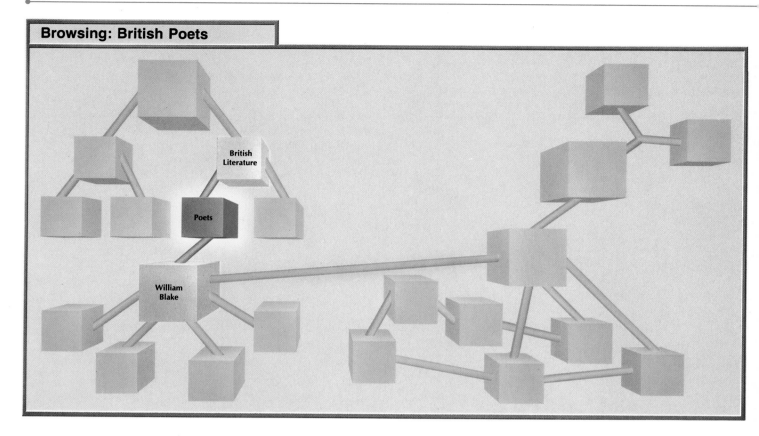

Browsing: William Blake

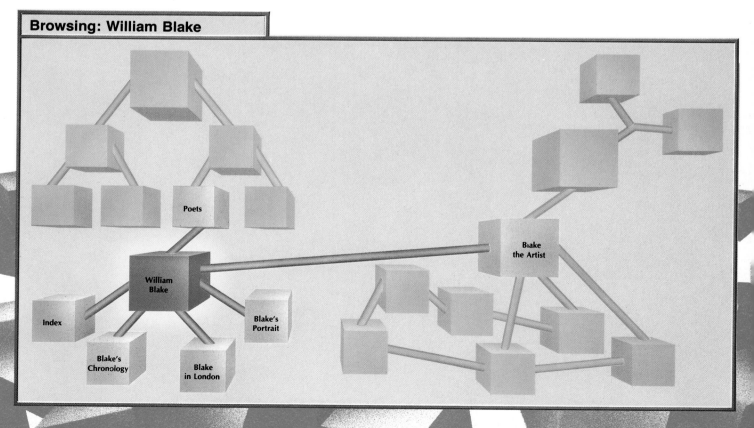

A Map for Traveling through the Web

The more nodes and links in a hypermedia system, the more extensive the information it contains and the deeper the exploration it can offer the researcher. But an elaborate system creates a complex network that may prove to be as confusing as the lanes and streets of an old city such as Boston or London. One expert refers to this as the disorientation problem—"the problem of knowing where you are in the network and how to get to some other place that you know (or think) exists in the network."

A simple menu, listing links from one node to others, may suffice. But most hypermedia systems need a map, known as a browser. In a basic system, the browser displays a sketch of all nodes and their connecting links. More commonly, however, it displays only a portion of the network then being used, showing nodes and links around the node that is under active investigation.

The browser also permits the user to leave a trail indicating the path of ideas that has been followed. It marks each node that has been examined so that the user can easily back up and take a different branch of study at some point.

Three steps in using a hypermedia browser are illustrated here. An investigation of British literature has led the researcher to a concentration on poets *(left, top drawing)*; the browser shows a link to Blake as a possible next step. From Blake *(left, bottom drawing)*, the researcher may move to one of several additional nodes. These include the previous node on British poets, four attribute links about Blake, and a node on Blake the artist. When the researcher chooses the latter node *(below)*, he may then investigate Blake's mysticism, his watercolors, or a volume of works.

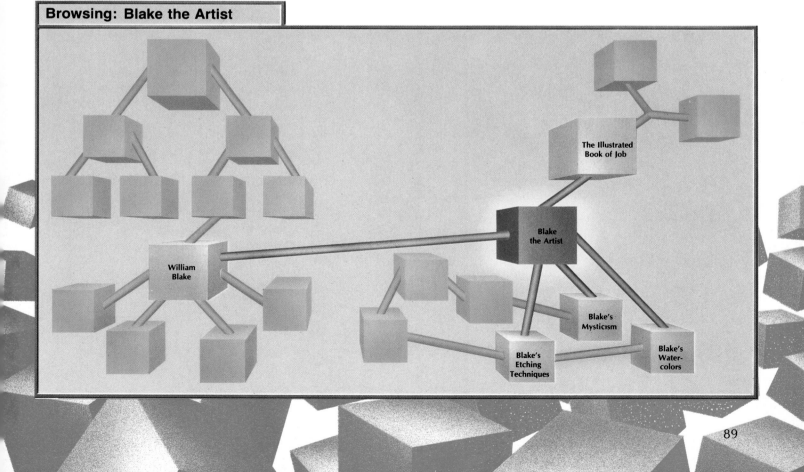

Browsing: Blake the Artist

The Illustrated Book of Job

Blake the Artist

William Blake

Blake's Mysticism

Blake's Etching Techniques

Blake's Water-colors

The Hypermedia Experience

Long before the invention of hypermedia systems, Vannevar Bush envisioned how nodes and links might be used to explore a subject—literature, history, technology, even archery.

A researcher seeking to compare the advantages of long and short bows, Bush wrote, first "runs through an encyclopedia, finds an interesting but sketchy article, leaves it projected. Next, in a history, he finds another pertinent item, and ties the two together. Thus he goes, building a trail of many items. Occasionally he inserts a comment of his own, either linking it into the main trail or joining it by a side trail to a

William Blake

Chronology

1757	William Bla 28 at 28 Br son of Jam a shopkee Baptized D James' Ch
c.1765-1767	Sees "a tree filled with angels" on Peckham Rye.
1772-1779	Apprenticed to James Basire, engraver. Probably lives with Basire's family at 31 Great Queen Street, Lincoln's Inn Fields. In 1774, begins sketching memorials in Westminster Abbey for Basire.
1779	October. Admitted as a student to the Royal Academy of Arts.
1780	June 6. Unwillingly caught in a mob storming Newgate Prison during anti-Catholic riots.
1782	August 18. Married to Catherine Boucher in St. Mary's Church, Battersea.
1783	Printing of *Poetical Sketches* arranged by John Flaxman and the Reverend and Mrs. Anthony Stephen Mathew.

A hypermedia exploration of Blake begins with a chronology of important events in his life and a look at his portrait, a watercolor painted by John Linnell in 1861. Because the chronology points to the great impact of Blake's personal philosophy on his art, the user calls up a commentary about the artist's spiritual beliefs *(below)* and several examples of his work: Blake's own interpretation of the Last Judgment *(right)* as a vision, his painting of that vision *(far right)*, and a catalog representation, with analysis, of his monoprint of the creation of Adam *(bottom right)*.

Blake's mysticism

So Blake was on firm ground when he believed that each man repeats in miniature the whole of spiritual history, past and to come. The Fall appears in the very act of birth, which is a division. Then for a while Man lives in the Earthly Paradise as a child; but the seeds of Error are in him: 'Man is born a Spectre or Satan'; and sooner or later he falls from Innocence into Experience, which is Death from Eternity. From this he is rescued by a Last Judgment—whether in a vision of mere Hope and Fear (as in *The Gates of Paradise*), or in a mystical revelation (as in the *Inventions to Job*), or not until death, depends upon the man himself.

Mystical revelation is the highest moment possible to the flesh. Blake often describes it, but says little more about it: such as how necessary it is, or how it may be induced. He must have realized what a rare thing it is. However, he felt that the same thing was mildly repeated in prayer and in art. The three modes of conversing with Paradise are Poetry, Painting, and Music; during the moment of inspiration, the artist is actually in Eden. Thus Eternity obtains in the flesh. 'What is Immortality but the things relating to the Spirit, which Lives Eternally? What is the Joy of Heaven but Improvement in things of The Spirit?' 'A Poet, a Painter, a Musician, an Architect; the man or woman who is not one of these is not a Christian.'

particular item. When it becomes evident that the elastic properties of available materials had a great deal to do with the bow, he branches off on a side trail, which takes him through textbooks on elasticity and tables of physical constants." In this way, the researcher "builds a trail of his interest through the maze of materials available to him."

How the same process can be applied today for a study of William Blake is illustrated below. The hypermedia system permits the user to jump quickly from idea to idea, pause to review definitions of terms, and dig into background infor-

mation. Without leaving his chair, the researcher learns about Blake, simultaneously creating an electronic notebook that reveals relationships not only between Blake's art and poetry but also between Blake's works and the philosophy of his contemporaries. This research and compilation has all occurred on the computer screen, and—perhaps equally important to a scholar—the evolution of the information's assembly can be easily retraced. Both reading and writing have become open-ended; there need be no conclusion to a journey through hypermedia.

The Last Judgment

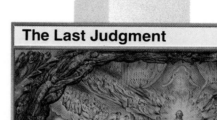

A Vision of the Last Judgment

The Last Judgment [will be] when all those are Cast away who trouble Religion with Questions concerning Good & Evil or Eating of the Tree of those Knowledges or Reasonings which hinder the Vision of God turning all into a Consuming fire. When Imaginative Art & Science & all Intellectual Gifts, all the Gifts of the Holy Ghost, are lookd upon as of no use & only Contention remains to Man then the Last Judgment begins & its Vision is seen by the Imaginative Eye of Every one according to the situation he holds.

[Page 68] The Last Judgment is not Fable or Allegory but Vision. Fable or Allegory are a totally distinct & inferior kind of Poetry. Vision or Imagination is a Representation of what Eternally Exists, Really & Unchangeably. Fable or Allegory is Formd by the daughters of Memory. Imagination is Surrounded by the daughters ̶ who in the aggregate are calld Jeru ̶ Fable is Allegory but what Critics ca ̶ Vision itself. [P 68].The Hebrew Bib ̶ pel of Jesus are not Allegory but Ete ̶ Imagination of All that Exists. Note ̶ ble or Allegory is Seldom without s ̶

Elohim Creating Adam

Elohim creating Adam
c.1795. Monoprint, with pen and watercolour. 17x21⅛in (42.1x53.6cm)

A most severe interpretation of the creation of man. Elohim is the Hebrew name for God in his aspect of justice. He is shown here as a terrifying, stone-like figure virtually dragging the protesting form of man from the world of the spirit into the enslavement of mortality.

London, Tate Gallery

Peepholes to the Future

The ultimate puzzle—predicting the future—has earned a reputation for obstinacy. No matter the form, from the ancient Greeks' reading of birds in flight to the medieval reliance on the utterances of soothsayers, reliable forecasting of events has remained elusive. Yet hope lives on, leading humankind to embrace a new and more sophisticated means of divination—the computer. Though some might claim that a computer, a flock of birds, and a clairvoyant offer equally dubious assessments of the future, the truth is that, in many instances, forecasts made with computers are superior to those attempted without them.

The sources of computer predictions are computer models, sets of complex mathematical equations that seek to capture the essence of social or physical phenomena. Such equations, although they are too difficult to solve by hand in any reasonable amount of time, succumb to a high-speed computer in a few hours or days.

The increasing abilities of computers to perform feats of mathematical computation or graphical representation that are far beyond human faculties have ushered in a golden age of forecasting. Computer models are being used to predict tomorrow's weather, next year's economic growth, and next century's atmospheric conditions. An elite handful of computer models have unveiled information that most likely would have remained inaccessible in other forms. For example, computer models were instrumental in the formulation of chaos theory, heralded in the late 1980s as a scientific watershed of the twentieth century. From storms in the earth's atmosphere to fluctuations in cotton prices, states this theory, many physical and social phenomena exhibit erratic and unpredictable behavior. Beneath the chaos, however, lurk limits to the disorder, boundaries that have been revealed chiefly by the workings of computer models.

Modeling the future or any phenomenon, be it orderly or chaotic, is an inexact science; many computer models have painted views of the future that proved to be unreasonably optimistic—or excessively dire—in light of actual events. However, as economist Stephen McNees of the Federal Reserve Bank of Boston remarked in 1986, "People will continue to use computer models until an obviously superior alternative comes along."

ANATOMY OF A MODEL

One of the most prominent uses of computer models is also one of the most practical: predicting the course of a nation's economy. The impetus for many of the first economic models sprang from the economic disaster of the Great Depression—and the universal desire never to repeat it.

In 1935, Dutch economist Jan Tinbergen embarked on a project that would win for him in 1969 the first Nobel prize ever awarded in economics. He developed a mathematical model of his country's economy, and in 1939 he built an expanded model to reflect the economic system of the United States. Calculated without the aid of computers, both models attempted to capture the workings of a national economy in the form of equations derived from data about the economy's past performance. Tinbergen's models were among the pioneering ventures that laid the foundation of modern econometrics—the study of economics using mathematical and statistical methods—and decades later they would inspire economists and computer scientists to join forces in fashioning a remarkably varied range of economic models.

Tinbergen's models contained two types of equations. Examples of the first variety are known as definitional equations. A typical definitional equation is the one for gross national product (GNP), an annual figure defined as being equal to all the money that consumers spend on goods and services, plus the money that individuals and businesses invest, plus the government's expenditures added to the nation's exports diminished by its imports.

The second type of equation, known as a stochastic equation, is descriptive in nature. Rather than defining a concept, it describes the relationship between one economic variable and a series of others. A widely used descriptive equation, for example, argues that the rate at which individuals purchase new homes hinges primarily on consumer income, housing prices, the prevailing mortgage rates, and other financing variables. To devise accurate descriptive equations, an economist examines such historical statistics as the extent to which increased interest rates have affected housing purchases in the past.

There are limits to this approach, however. Because no descriptive equation can hope to incorporate every factor governing economic behavior, most of them have "add factors" appended to represent such nuances as consumer confidence in the economy or investment expectations. Noticing a rising tide of investor optimism, for example, Tinbergen might have adjusted the add factor for a descriptive equation to a higher value than he would have used during a period of pessimism. Detractors occasionally refer to add factors as fudge factors, but such adjustments are crucial to any accuracy that an econometric model might aspire to. Without them, important information would be excluded, and deciding how to adjust add factors demands the judgment of a skilled economist.

Accompanying the two types of equations in Tinbergen's models were two types of variables. Some represented factors that originated outside the model— weather conditions, for example, or governmental tax and trade policies—and were termed exogenous, or external. Because Tinbergen did not intend his models to predict external variables, he had to estimate values for them and then insert the numbers into the equations. Endogenous, or internal, variables, on the other hand, represented the unknown quantities—the unemployment rate, say, or the pace of economic growth—that Tinbergen wished to predict. When supplied with the current value of external variables, his models calculated the future values of internal variables.

THE MAKING OF AN ECONOMETRICIAN

World War II prevented Jan Tinbergen from testing his model of the U.S. economy, but his ideas became common currency among American economists who shared the Dutchman's interest in forecasting. One of them, a visionary economist named Lawrence Klein, would bring Tinbergen's methods into the computer age. "As a youth of the Depression," wrote Klein upon receiving his own Nobel prize for economics in 1980, "I wanted intensely to have some understanding of what was going on around me." Klein had earned a doctorate in economics from the Massachusetts Institute of Technology in just two years, a record for the department. In 1946, building on Tinbergen's earlier work, he produced his own mathematical model of the U.S. economy.

Three years after joining the University of Michigan as an economics professor in 1949, Klein worked with a graduate student named Arthur Goldberger to complete a new model of the U.S. economy. The Klein-Goldberger model was sophisticated by the standards of the day; it incorporated twenty-five equations and fourteen external variables, whose interplay projected the health of the U.S. economy year by year into the future. Of more enduring import, the model was the first of its kind to employ computers. In the early 1950s, digital machines were just becoming available to university researchers. Then as now, the machines were ideally suited to the rote statistical tasks—processing reams of data on interest rates, foreign trade, production, and employment, for example—that are required to create an econometric model. Klein gladly assigned such data analysis to a card-programmed IBM electronic computer.

In 1954, Klein ran afoul of Senator Joseph McCarthy, then at the height of his personal crusade against suspected communists in the United States. Testifying before the House Committee on Un-American Activities, Klein revealed that in 1945 he had been asked to teach a course on Marxist economics to a group of people in his Chicago neighborhood. Eager to explain his differences with Marx's economics, Klein had accepted. He had then been informed that because everyone taking the course was a member of the Communist party, he too would have to join. Young and naive, Klein had done just that, and he had remained a party member until he left Chicago in 1947.

Upon learning of Klein's testimony, administrators at the University of Michigan let him know that tenure was out of the question. Klein promptly quit his job and moved to England. "I didn't have to leave the country," he recalled in 1975. "I left because I felt Michigan hadn't taken a tough enough stand on academic freedom."

As a researcher and lecturer at Oxford University, Klein devised several models of the British economy and bequeathed his methods to a generation of British followers. In 1958, Klein returned to the United States to accept a teaching post at the University of Pennsylvania's Wharton School of Business. There he fashioned a model that could make quarterly forecasts, rather than the annual forecasts customary before. And with the increasing availability of computers, Klein also computerized more and more of the model-making process.

As Klein's model took shape at the Wharton School, a Brown University graduate student named Michael Evans was designing his own model of the U.S. economy. Upon receiving his Ph.D. in the spring of 1963, Evans joined the Wharton School as an assistant professor, bringing his model with him. The following autumn, running Klein's and Evans's models in concert, the Wharton School began to issue forecasts of the U.S. economy eight quarters into the future. Within a year, Klein and Evans had merged their two models into a single large one of seventy-six equations containing forty-two external variables. Known as

the Wharton, or
merged, model,
it was the first in
a series of Wharton
School economic forecasting tools that have
produced quarterly economic projections ever since.

TACTICS FOR A CRYSTAL BALL

As a professor of economics at Wharton, Klein quickly earned the tenure that had been denied him at Michigan. He also extended his efforts beyond the Wharton model, joining a group of economists from around the country who, in the early 1960s, set out to construct the most comprehensive economic model ever built. Sponsored by the Brookings Institution, the project pioneered a number of techniques that would shape the future of econometric modeling.

The most important was the computerization of a method for solving large numbers of interrelated equations. Known as the Gauss-Seidel technique after the two nineteenth-century mathematicians, Karl Gauss and Philipp Ludwig von Seidel, who developed it, the method works from estimates for the variables in question. When the set of equations is solved for these values, inconsistencies arise in the solutions, showing that the estimates are incorrect. Adjustments are made in the values, and the procedure is repeated. After a number of tries— sometimes as few as forty and rarely more than a hundred—the true values of the variables are revealed.

When the Brookings model was completed in 1964, it contained 226 equations. No army of humans could cope with the calculations necessary to solve them, yet a computer program employing the Gauss-Seidel technique could provide an answer in minutes. Drawn by such quickness, more and more econometricians abandoned pencil and paper for computers to run their models. By 1968, Klein and Evans reported, computers had wrought "an enormous technological change in the conduct of modern econometric research."

The marriage of computers and economics dazzled corporate and government planners. Now, they could quickly observe how a hypothetical tax cut might affect hundreds of economic variables, gauge the impact higher interest rates might have on investment, or trace the effects higher energy prices might have on the prices of raw materials. Within one brief decade, econometric modeling had evolved from an academic exercise into a powerful economic tool.

MODELS AND THE PROFIT MOTIVE

The mid-1960s were boom years for the United States economy, and econometric models proved adept at forecasting that expansion, a talent not lost on the nation's business community—or on a number of entrepreneurs who saw commercial potential in prophesying the economic future for industry and government. Among those who moved to supply such services was Otto Eckstein, a Harvard University economics professor who had advised President Lyndon Johnson on economic matters from 1964 to 1966. In late 1968, Eckstein and partner Donald Marron founded Data Resources, Inc. (DRI), to sell economic forecasts. Eckstein enlisted the aid of several economists who had worked on the Brookings model, and the group constructed a new model of the U.S. economy and a large database geared to the needs of corporate and government planners.

In 1969, Eckstein arranged for DRI's model and database to be loaded into a Burroughs B5500 mainframe computer. He then made both the model and the database available to clients through an arrangement known as time-sharing. With computers still too expensive for most businesses to own one, time-sharing provided the benefits of computing at a reasonable price. Telephone lines connected terminals in a time-sharing subscriber's offices to a central computer, enabling scores of people to share in the computational power of one machine.

For $1,500 to $12,000 per year, depending on the range of services desired, DRI customers could run the model using different assumptions about the economy's future behavior, or they could run their own models using information drawn from DRI's database. So comprehensive was this database, recalled economist Douglas Hale in 1988, that some government agencies acquired aggregate data from it that the agencies themselves had provided to DRI in piecemeal form. Corporate and government economists hungrily consumed DRI's forecasts and data, enabling the company to grow more than 50 percent a year in the early 1970s. By the time Eckstein sold DRI to McGraw-Hill in 1979, his company was worth more than $100 million.

Eckstein was not the only person to profit from predicting the economic future. Michael Evans, who had collaborated with Lawrence Klein on the Wharton model in 1963, started up an econometric firm in 1969. Lacking the name recognition that Eckstein had earned as a presidential adviser, Evans soon became strapped for funds, and in 1971 he sold his company to the Chase Manhattan Bank. Renamed Chase Econometric Associates, the firm issued a series of unerring forecasts in the early 1970s that helped the company prosper.

Lawrence Klein, too, entered the field. In 1969, the Wharton School split off its econometric-modeling activities into a nonprofit corporation known as Wharton Econometric Forecasting Associates (WEFA). With DRI and Chase, WEFA rounded out the "Big Three" of econometric modeling firms. By the close of the 1970s, the trio would be doing more than $120 million worth of business a year.

A RUDE AWAKENING

While econometric modeling firms did a brisk business in the early 1970s, the U.S. economy grew sluggish, overextended by the simultaneous funding of the Vietnam War and President Johnson's War on Poverty. Then, in 1973, the Arab countries invaded Israel in the Yom Kippur War, and the Organization of Petroleum Exporting Countries (OPEC) imposed an embargo on oil shipments to the United States. Within a few months, the price of crude oil had jumped from three dollars a barrel to nearly twelve dollars a barrel.

Here was a situation that seemed tailor-made for econometric modeling. By considering the increased price of oil—an external variable—econometric models should have been able to predict how the rest of the economy would react. But they failed, and failed dismally. WEFA's guess at the inflation rate, the best of a group that predicted about six percent, was eight percent; inflation soared instead into the double digits. The models forecast that the economy would continue to grow at a slow rate; it plunged instead into a deep recession.

Although the exact causes of the models' poor showing remained difficult to identify, it was clear that one overriding condition—the inherent instability of the economy itself—had played hob with the models' projections. Economists continue to debate the full magnitude of the economy's fluctuations over time, yet most members of the profession agree that because econometric models use historical data to predict the future, they work best when history repeats itself. Yet rarely is history so accommodating. Industries prosper and decline. An emphasis on manufacturing evolves into an accent on services. The government passes new tax or trade laws. Nor can any model ever accurately forecast the sudden economic jolts that modelers refer to as "outliers"—a drought in the Midwest, for example, or a war in the Middle East.

Whatever the causes, the lackluster performance of economic forecasting in the face of higher oil prices prompted the consumers of econometric forecasts to take a more critical view of the predictions' sources. Economists themselves admitted that their crystal ball may have been oversold, something they had been reluctant to concede in the models' halcyon days. "From where I sit," pronounced Arthur Okun, a former chairman of the President's Council of Economic Advisers, "the econometric models just don't reflect the real world."

As the U.S. economy adjusted to higher energy prices brought on by the oil embargo, econometric models fared somewhat better in their forecasts. During 1976 and 1977, DRI, Chase Econometrics, and WEFA erred less than one percent in their predictions of inflation, unemployment, and the gross national product. But the aura had faded, and the Big Three would never regain the stature—or the profits—that they had enjoyed for so brief a time.

MODELING ON A MICRO

The *coup de grâce* for many time-sharing systems would be delivered by personal computers. The seeds of PC-based econometric models had in fact been germinating for some time. At Princeton University in the early 1970s, for example, an economist named Ray Fair devised a small model containing just twenty equations, which ran on the college's IBM 7094 mainframe. Concerned that his model produce forecasts of maximum scientific objectivity, Fair had opted to exclude add factors. Partly as a result, his model did a poor job of predicting the economy.

Yet Fair's experience with small models would pay an unexpected dividend. As personal computers became steadily cheaper and more powerful in the late 1970s, Fair recognized that PCs rather than mainframes could be used to solve econometric models. In 1981, he was among the first econometricians to release an econometric model that could be run on a personal computer. It consisted of 128 equations and cost a fraction of the price of mainframe time-sharing services. Every three months, Fair mailed to users of his model a floppy disk containing quarterly updates of economic data that they could plug into the model's equations. Resourceful customers could combine Fair's model with models they had built themselves.

For the Big Three econometric firms, the implications were obvious. Few clients, they feared, would pay for time-sharing when the same capabilities had become available for personal computers at a fraction of the cost. As if to underscore that concern, a PC-based computer program appeared in 1984 that could solve econometric models consisting of thousands of equations. Striving to remain competitive, Wharton, Chase, and DRI released PC-based versions of their own models. But sales of software for individual PCs could not match the sizable revenues the Big Three had collected from mainframe time-sharing. McGraw-Hill, the company that had bought DRI from Otto Eckstein, scattered the firm's functions throughout its corporate divisions. Chase Econometrics, for its part, suffered two years of heavy losses before merging with Wharton Econometric Forecasting Associates to form a new—and considerably leaner—company.

AN ENGINEER TURNS MODELER

The econometric approach—extrapolating from historical data to forecast economic trends—is just one of many strategies that computer modelers have adopted in their efforts to predict the future. A divergent approach, known as system dynamics, often disregards the historical record as inapplicable to a world that can change rapidly and drastically in response to unprecedented stimuli such as the Arab oil embargo. To allow for the possibility of sudden and complex interactions, a system-dynamics modeler tries to replicate the underlying structure of a social system. If the system-dynamics model is a good one, it will be able to reproduce the historical behavior of the system rather than simply use that behavior as an input. Typically, a system dynamicist draws on expert opinion—and even on personal observation—to describe the system and to establish the relationships among its variables.

Because of this willingness to proceed without the historically grounded statistical analysis that underpins econometric models, economist Lawrence Klein, for one, has characterized system dynamics as "stylizing the facts." System dynamicists reply that many of the most important relationships in any social system have never been quantified, and that to omit them from a model is to assume—incorrectly—that they will have no effect. Whatever the merits of the method, system dynamics will likely remain embroiled in controversy, not only because of its techinques but also because of its tendency to turn out gloomy prognostications.

The father of system dynamics is a well-known figure in the history of computing. Born into a Nebraska cattle-ranching family, Jay Forrester made a name for himself at M.I.T. in 1944, when at twenty-six he led a team of engineers in building the world's first computer-controlled flight simulator. Five years later, he became one of the architects of magnetic-core memories, which would serve as the dominant form of computer memory for the next two decades. But by the mid-1950s, Forrester had begun to seek something beyond the mechanical challenge of building computers; he turned instead to their application.

The first social systems Forrester modeled were in the business world. One model, for instance, examined how delayed deliveries of a company's product to retailers can affect the firm's plans for expansion. When the company's managers believe that low inventory is a necessary safeguard against business downturns, for example, the product's sales may fall because of a backlog of orders. The company's management may then conclude that not enough demand exists to justify expanding production capacity, when the limited sales

A Luxuriance of Detail

The marriage of computer and high-resolution graphics has produced a nascent branch of mathematics called fractal geometry. Named for a Latin word meaning irregular or fragmented, fractal geometry explores a world of crinkly, convoluted shapes far removed from the straight lines and smooth curves of traditional Euclidean geometry. Fractal shapes bear a striking resemblance to structures in nature—the billowing of clouds, the jagged peaks of mountains, the tortuous edges of a coastline. Equally remarkable, a fractal shape reveals ever-finer detail as it is magnified, just as a closer look at an

object in nature discloses features unseen at greater distances

A spectacular example of fractals is known as the Mandelbrot set, named for Benoit Mandelbrot, the acknowledged father of fractal geometry. Converted by a computer from numbers into an image, the Mandelbrot set becomes the ornately edged ladybug shape shown on these and the following pages. Each point contains whirls and eddies of ever-more-complex structure. When magnified 120,000 times *(overleaf)*, the Mandelbrot set is seen to contain the miniature ladybugs, each ornamented with galaxies of even tinier detail

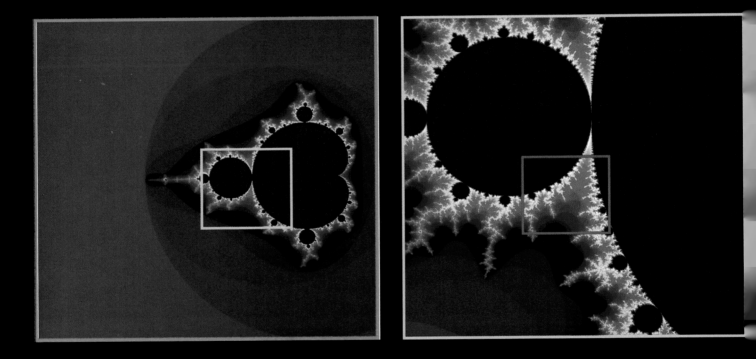

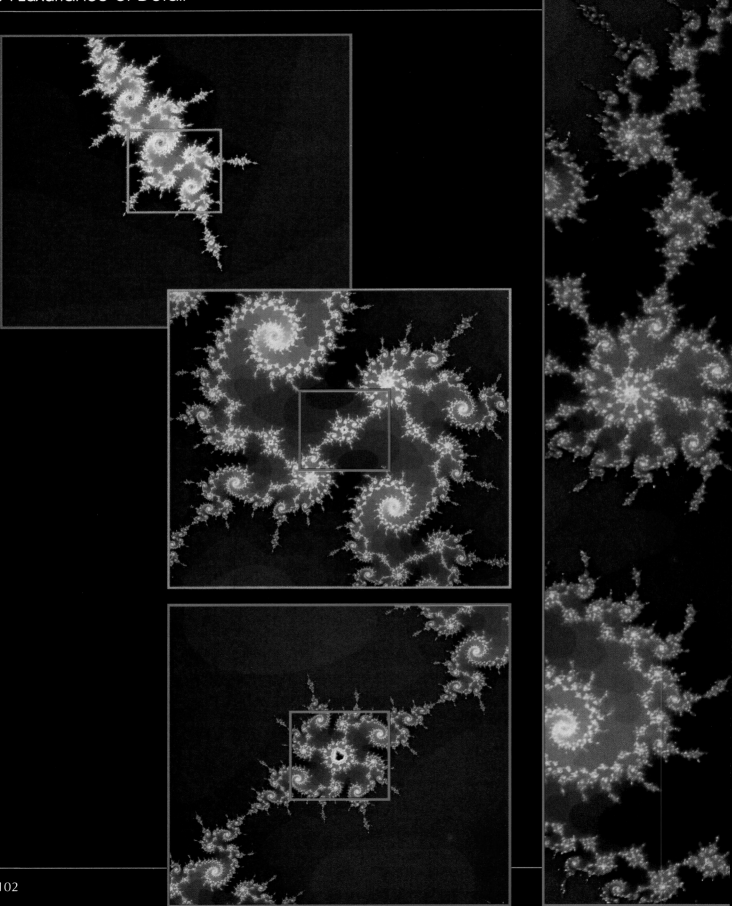

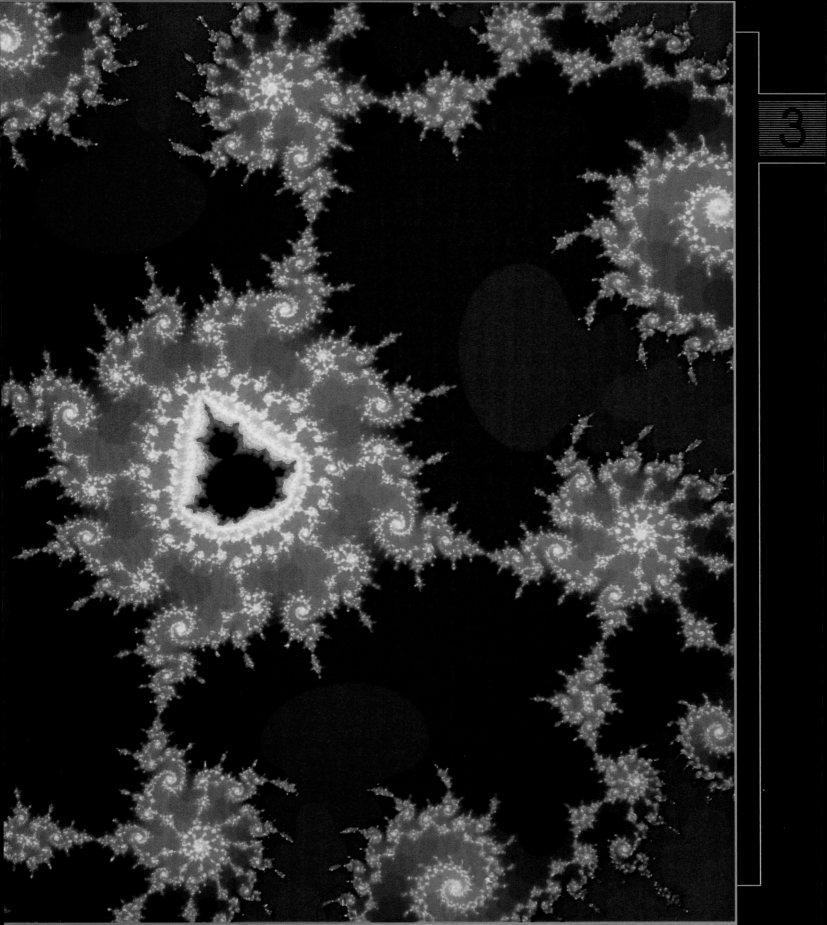

actually are a result of management's inventory policies. In the workaday world of corporate life, Forrester had observed, such fundamental causes and effects tend to remain obscured by the system's overall complexity. But when they are translated into mathematical equations and modeled on a computer, he was convinced, they would become readily apparent.

The pioneer of system dynamics did not have to wait long for a chance to test his theory. In the 1950s, when Digital Equipment Corporation (DEC) president Kenneth Olsen asked Forrester to join DEC's board of directors, Forrester built a system-dynamics model to guide that company's corporate strategy. The model proved instrumental, Forrester later stated, in helping DEC to formulate its policies for pricing and product quality, which in turn helped the company grow to become the world's second-largest computer manufacturer in 1988.

Since the mid-1960s, practitioners of the system-dynamics philosophy have developed computer models for a wide variety of social systems, from the growth and stagnation of cities to the mechanics of the arms race between the United States and the Soviet Union. Yet system dynamics received universal attention only when it attempted to replicate the largest social system of all—the world.

TAKING ON THE WORLD

Forrester was drawn to global modeling by an international activist organization known as the Club of Rome. The club's thirty founding members included scientists, industrialists, educators, and government officials from all over the world who had come together in 1968 to combat humanity's seemingly self-destructive tendencies. In 1970, the Club of Rome held a meeting in Bern, Switzerland, to discuss a set of global problems—chiefly overpopulation, environmental degradation, and resource depletion—that the group termed the "world problematique," or the predicament of mankind. One of Forrester's colleagues at M.I.T. happened to be on the club's executive committee, and he invited Forrester to address the meeting on how system dynamics might help analyze the organization's concerns. Members thought enough of Forrester's presentation to accept his invitation to visit the M.I.T. campus in Cambridge, Massachusetts, for a demonstration of system dynamics in action.

On the return flight to Boston, Forrester worked out the broad outlines of a system-dynamics model that addressed several major components of the world problematique. Using a computer terminal in his suburban Concord home that was connected to the time-sharing mainframe computer on M.I.T.'s Cambridge campus, he refined the model over the next two weekends. By the time the club members arrived, Forrester's preliminary global model was able to simulate the interactions among five worldwide sectors—population, economic growth, food production, pollution, and natural resources—from 1900 into the twenty-first century. The model's utility was demonstrated by one of its initial runs, during which the model simulated behavior for the five sectors from 1900 to 1970 that closely paralleled the behavior those sectors had actually exhibited in that period. The model also simulated the sectors' interaction 100 years into the future, with results that warned of trouble ahead.

Taken with the demonstration, the Club of Rome offered to fund the model's completion. Forrester, however, had previously committed himself to a project applying system dynamics to cities, so he assigned much of the work on the global model to a team headed by a twenty-nine-year-old former graduate student, Dennis Meadows, and his biophysicist wife, Donella. The Meadows report, published in 1972 as *The Limits to Growth,* was ultimately translated into twenty-three languages and sold more than three million copies.

The report's findings were every bit as dramatic as its sales. *The Limits to Growth* described a computer model, based on the preliminary model demonstrated in Boston for the Club of Rome, that could analyze and forecast the relationships among the same five global sectors that Forrester had identified earlier. The model examined the mutual and simultaneous feedbacks of all these sectors, whose interaction made for some extraordinarily complex dynamics.

Run on a computer, the global model projected an alarming chain of events. The earth would exhaust its stock of natural resources sometime around 2020, predicted the model; unless steps were taken immediately to limit births, preserve the environment, and recycle materials, world population would outstrip the planet's ability to support it and would fall precipitously soon thereafter.

The model's apocalyptic tenor stemmed in part from its designers' assumption that the relationships among the five major sectors would continue to hold true. The equation describing the effect of the standard of living on world birth rate, for example, was "specified initially," meaning that it remained largely unchanged throughout the model run. In the actual course of human events, however, such constancy is unknown. A population's customary response to some drastic decline in its standard of living—precipitated by a severe economic depression, for example, or by war—is a corresponding drop in the population's overall birth rate. Yet the global model had accounted only marginally for such variability in the relationship.

For shortcomings such as these—and because the global model was widely distributed to anyone who wanted it—*The Limits to Growth* was "one of the most criticized models of all time," acknowledged Donella Meadows in 1982. Although environmentalists heartily seconded its findings, other researchers branded its scientific content as "virtually zero." Economists in particular assailed the lack of hard data in the model. Yale economics professor Martin Shubik, for instance, wrote that Forrester's approach was "energetic, simplistic, and superficially attractive, but nonetheless dangerously wrong." Yet as the critical maelstrom made clear, Forrester had cast light on a crucial issue through the intensely focused beam of a computer model.

UP IN THE AIR

Models based on econometrics or system dynamics are invariably handicapped in trying to describe social systems, which remain inherently complex and poorly understood. As scientists in many other fields have found out, equally nettlesome difficulties plague models of physical systems and attempts to predict their future.

Since 1974, for example, scientists had speculated that a family of chemicals known as chlorofluorocarbons (CFCs), which consist of chlorine, fluorine, and carbon, might be destroying the atmospheric ozone that makes life on earth possible. The best-known CFC is Freon®, invented in 1928 by a chemist working for the Frigidaire Division of General Motors. The GM chemist was seeking an inert, nontoxic substitute for the flammable, poisonous chemicals then used as refrigerants. In a demonstration of Freon's noncombustible nature at a meeting of the American Chemical Society in 1930, the chemist blew out a candle with a mouthful of Freon gas. Since that time, Freon and other CFCs have been used not only as chilling agents in air conditioners and refrigerators but also as propellants in spray cans, as an ingredient of the insulating foam that makes up fast-food containers, and even as cleaning solvents for semiconductor chips. The chemical industry worldwide produces about a million tons of CFCs per year, nearly all of which eventually enters the atmosphere.

Chlorofluorocarbons are carried into the stratosphere—the rarefied shell of the atmosphere that extends from six miles to thirty miles above the surface of the earth—through the action of global air currents. At those high altitudes, the CFCs encounter the full force of the sun's ultraviolet rays for the first time, and the radiation decomposes them into their constituent elements. One of them, chlorine, combines with an important component of the stratosphere, a three-atom molecule of oxygen called ozone, to form molecules of oxygen and chlorine monoxide. Further chemical reactions separate the chlorine atoms in the chlorine monoxide from their oxygen partners, permitting the chlorine to combine with still more ozone. In this way, each chlorine atom can destroy as many as 100,000 ozone molecules before it sinks into the denser air below and is washed from the atmosphere by rain.

In the lower atmosphere, ozone is a powerful pollutant that irritates the eyes and throat. In the stratosphere, however, ozone has a beneficial effect: It absorbs the sun's harmful rays of ultraviolet light, shielding the surface of the planet below—and all living things upon it—from this potentially lethal radiation.

THE DATA THAT NO ONE BELIEVED

For more than a decade, the supposition that CFCs were destroying the ozone remained just that—a supposition. The depredations of CFCs were not immediately evident; most such molecules require ten years or more to migrate into the stratosphere where they wreak their damage. To complicate matters, difficulties could be expected in distinguishing CFC-induced ozone losses from natural fluctuations in ozone levels.

In May 1985, however, a British scientist named Joseph Farman reported that he had been measuring stratospheric ozone levels above his research station in Antarctica for nearly three decades, and that beginning in the mid-1970s he had begun to detect marked decreases in those levels. The losses were decidedly seasonal, he had observed, with the ozone reaching its nadir in the Antarctic spring—September through November—then gradually replenishing itself until the next killing season. By 1984, the concentration of ozone molecules over the continent had dropped by 40 percent from the level first recorded in 1958. Farman had waited years to go public, he said, because he had been unable to verify the readings collected by his instruments. Then as now, satellites could not orbit low enough to collect samples of the stratosphere, and research aircraft of the day could not fly high enough. Lacking the means to assay the stratosphere directly, Farman had been forced to rely on measurements taken indirectly and from a distance—circumstances almost guaranteed to cast doubt on unusual or unexpected readings.

As it turned out, a number of other researchers had also measured an ozone "hole" in the stratosphere above the southernmost continent. But since no one else had reported any similar results, these researchers, too, had doubted the reliability of their instruments. Even the *Nimbus 7* satellite, a NASA spacecraft that estimates ozone levels by measuring ultraviolet sunlight reflected from the earth and its atmosphere, had detected decreased levels of Antarctic ozone for several years. One year, scientists had decided to double-check the satellite's measurements against those taken by instruments on the ground. The ground readings, however, had been incorrectly recorded, leading the scientists to conclude that the measuring device aboard *Nimbus 7* must have been mistaken.

Further obscuring the truth were the computer models that scientists had been using since 1970 or so to predict ozone losses. Fashioned from equations that describe the interactions among the stratosphere's twenty or thirty most common chemical elements, these models showed that CFCs being released into the atmosphere in the early 1970s should cause ozone losses of no more than one or two percent, with greater effects expected as the level of CFCs increased. That none of the models predicted the severity of the Antarctic ozone losses observed by Farman only lengthened the shadow cast on the measurements.

No sooner had Farman announced his findings than the computer models came under scrutiny. There were two possible sources of error. The first was a failure to understand the true nature of the chemistry between CFCs and ozone. Perhaps, researchers speculated, some mechanism that proceeded much faster than the breakdown of ozone molecules by chlorine from the CFCs was responsible for the hole. But flights by a modified U-2 spy plane—whose altitude ceiling of thirteen miles enabled it to fly right into the ozone hole to collect air samples—turned up high concentrations of chlorine monoxide, implicating CFCs as the prime culprit of the ozone's depletion. The chemists therefore seemed to be on the right track.

The second possible oversight was a change in the prevailing winds. If an updraft chanced to develop every spring over Antarctica—because of the warming trend that is taking place in the earth's climate, for example—ozone-poor air from beneath the stratosphere might well up and create the hole. To test this theory, atmospheric scientists turned to another kind of computer model, known as a general-circulation model. Such models, employed every day in weather forecasting, treat the earth's atmosphere as a gigantic three-dimensional grid. Each point in the grid is assigned a temperature, humidity, and wind speed. (The data is collected by a globe-girdling network of ground stations, weather balloons, and satellites.) When supplied with these measurements, the computer predicts how the atmosphere can be expected to circulate during the next twenty-four hours. But when researchers applied a general-circulation model to the atmosphere above Antarctica, they determined that there was no influx of ozone-poor air from below.

However, a closer examination of the Antarctic atmosphere finally revealed the chemical mechanism accelerating the ozone's disappearance. Every winter, a vortex of air forms over the continent, effectively isolating its atmosphere. The effect of this solitary confinement is to drive the normally frigid winter temperatures of the Antarctic stratosphere even lower, because the vortex shuts off the exchange of air that takes place during the rest of the year between the earth's warmer middle latitudes and its polar regions. Yet the vortex was not the only cooling agent; the lack of sunlight during the polar winter was pushing the stratospheric temperatures lower still. When the temperature of the Antarctic stratosphere fell below about $-80°$ C.—the condensation point of water in that lightly pressurized realm—the water vapor present in the stratosphere was converted into wispy clouds.

It was these polar stratospheric clouds, or PSCs as they became infamously known to atmospheric scientists, that were creating a theater for the ozone's destruction. Particles of ice in the PSCs served as catalytic surfaces, converting the chlorine atoms into a form that, when exposed to the sunlight that returns in the Antarctic spring, made the chlorine combine much more readily with the ozone, thus hastening its destruction. The ice particles in the PSCs were playing a secondary abettor's role as well: They tended to gravitationally settle out of the stratosphere, taking with them nitrogen oxides that, had they remained on the scene, would have bonded with the predatory chlorine and helped to inhibit its ravages of the ozone. The complexity of the clouds' formation and the intricacy of their enabling role in the ozone's depletion had combined to veil the process from even the most foresighted of atmospheric-model designers. When new equations were inserted in the models to account for the clouds, the models came much closer to predicting the ozone losses observed.

The Antarctic ozone hole made atmospheric scientists skittish. If clouds could accelerate ozone depletion above the South Pole, they theorized, perhaps other, equally unanticipated reactions were causing losses of ozone somewhere else. Sure enough, just a few months after the May 1985 announcement of the ozone hole's existence, researchers reported that ozone levels in the planet's high northern latitudes seemed to have dropped by several percent since the 1970s. Again the observed decreases were more severe than the models had predicted, prompting a renewed search for effects that the modelers might have incorrectly weighted—or altogether overlooked.

MODELS OF UNPREDICTABILITY

Ozone-depletion models and others like them are valuable tools that allow scientists to crack puzzles that would be unyielding without assistance from computers. But in some areas of science, computer models are more than tools; they are instruments that afford new views of reality. Perhaps nowhere is this truer than in the realm of chaos theory.

This new branch of science was almost entirely unknown before computers. Chaos theory as it is defined today began with a simple, general-circulation model of the atmosphere, which M.I.T. meteorologist Edward N. Lorenz was running in 1960 on a slow, somewhat unreliable (it broke down about once a week) computer called a Royal McBee. Lorenz, a mathematician by training, had been put to work as a weather forecaster upon volunteering for Army Air Corps service in World War II. Intrigued by the mysteries of weather prediction, he remained a meteorologist after the war.

Lorenz was trying to do something that no one had contemplated before: to build a computer model of the atmosphere that would never repeat itself, that would produce a variety of weather patterns almost as endless as those observed in the real world. It was questionable whether a computer model—at best no more than a simplified representation of the atmosphere—could do any such thing. A model might be able to produce tremendous complexity, but mathematical intuition suggested that sooner or later it would start to repeat itself.

Lorenz found otherwise. Using a set of twelve equations that described much of the physics of the atmosphere, he fashioned a computer model exhibiting inexhaustible variations. As the model ran, the Royal McBee churned out day after day of changing weather, always familiar but never the same.

One day Lorenz decided to extend an earlier run of the model in order to examine it at greater length. To save time, he restarted the model in the middle, using intermediate results typed into the computer from a printout of the original run. He then walked down the hall for a cup of coffee.

When Lorenz returned to the computer, he was perplexed by the new printout. He had expected it to be identical to the old one, since the model had processed the same numbers for both runs. Yet after predicting a few days of weather that matched the old run, the fresh printout veered steadily into a new weather pattern.

Lorenz then remembered that to save space, the printout showed results to three decimal places, whereas the computer manipulated numbers internally to six decimal places. Upon entering the intermediate results into the computer, Lorenz had used the less precise value. Even though they were extremely small, the differences between the two sets of numbers had caused a drastic divergence in weather patterns within a surprisingly short interval—about two months of simulated time. Lorenz recognized that inaccuracies in atmospheric readings taken at weather stations far exceeded the errors that he had introduced in the rerun of his computer model. "I knew right then," Lorenz recollected in

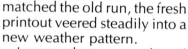

M.I.T. meteorologist Edward Lorenz, a pioneer of modern chaos theory, examines a printout generated by his 1960 computer model of weather patterns in the Northern Hemisphere. The red line represents the computer's projections of the difference in speed between westerly winds at high and low latitudes, while the blue line represents the computer's average predicted speed for those winds.

1984, "that if the real atmosphere behaved like this, long-range weather forecasting was impossible."

The phenomenon that Lorenz discovered has since been dubbed the Butterfly Effect: A butterfly flapping its wings in Beijing today may affect the weather in London next week. Better known to investigators of chaos theory as "sensitive dependence on initial conditions," the Butterfly Effect is now widely recognized as a hallmark of this new science. Because the calculations necessary to reveal the effect exceed the capacity of humans to do arithmetic, the phenomenon might never have been noticed were it not for the computer.

ORDER AMID CHAOS

Lorenz became intrigued with his equations' unpredictability. Curious to isolate the root of the chaotic behavior he had observed, the meteorologist began a search for the smallest number of equations that would demonstrate sensitive dependence on initial conditions. Following up on a suggestion by his friend Barry Saltzman, a research meteorologist in Hartford, Connecticut, Lorenz settled on three equations in three variables. Having satisfied himself that the equations displayed evidence of chaos, Lorenz then plotted as a three-dimensional graph the Royal McBee's solutions to those equations. Half expecting to see results randomly scattered about the graph, he noticed instead a striking three-dimensional shape on which all the solutions fell (pages 113-121).

The Lorenz attractor, as the shape became known for its seemingly magnetic pull on the equations' results, represented the limits to chaos. Although Lorenz could not predict where the solution for a set of initial conditions might fall within the shape, he could count on none of the solutions' falling outside the shape. Applied to the weather, for example, this principle accounts both for the difficulty in forecasting two weeks into the future whether rain or sunshine will prevail, and for the ease of discounting the possibility of a July snowfall in New York.

A small circle of meteorologists were quick to appreciate the significance of Lorenz's work. Not until his results gained wider attention in the 1970s, however, did the field of chaos—as mathematicians James Yorke and Tien-Yien Li of the University of Maryland christened it in 1975—finally take off. The formulation of chaos theory was pursued with especial vigor at the University of California at Santa Cruz, where in 1977 a thirty-one-year-old physics graduate student named Robert Shaw set up his computer to solve a set of three equations that a friend had urged him to investigate.

Although the friend—physicist William Burke—neglected to mention it at the time, the trio of equations he had handed Shaw were the same three that had conspired to create the oddly shaped attractor discovered by Lorenz a decade and a half earlier. As recounted by James Gleick in his 1987 book, Chaos, Burke had obtained the equations from one of Lorenz's acquaintances, astrophysicist Edward Spiegel, whose interest in the equations stemmed primarily from the quirky melody they produced when converted into musical form. Burke pressed the equations on Shaw because he wanted to see the Lorenz attractor take shape on a computer screen rather than listen to it trill from a hi-fi set.

Shaw in 1977 was just a few months away from completing his doctoral dissertation on superconductivity. But his academic career had frequently been interrupted before—by a stint in the army, by life on a commune, by long hours spent

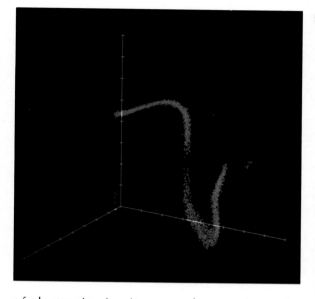

This saxophone-shaped image, captured by physicists at the University of California in 1984, revealed that a fundamental order underlies the apparently chaotic dripping of a water faucet. The image was generated by plotting on a three-dimensional graph successive triplets of the time intervals between water drops. For each point, the X coordinate is the time that elapsed between the faucet's first and second drops; the Y coordinate represents the interval between the second and third drops; and the Z coordinate denotes the interval between drops three and four. The physicists used the resulting pattern of points, called a strange attractor, as the basis for a computer model designed to replicate the faucet's behavior.

improvising at his piano. Now, the interplay of Lorenz's equations in his computer threatened to sidetrack Shaw again.

Shaw was using an analog computer, a denizen of computing's nearly forgotten byways. Most computers, being digital in nature, operate by reducing every problem to the on-off, yes-no language of binary code. In an analog computer, by contrast, a number is represented not as ones and zeros but as some continuously varying quantity—the amount of charge in an electrical component known as a capacitor, for instance. Within the limits of electronic circuits, a number can be assigned an infinity of values.

Analog computers have played only cameo roles in the drama of contemporary computing partly because of their imprecision: Two different analog computers typically produce two different answers to the same problem. The disparate results arise from mechanical subtleties—a fractional divergence in the relative diameter of electrical wires in the two machines, for example—that have no effect on the repeatability of results produced by digital computers.

Outmoded the analog computer may be, but it does have one thing going for it: The machine is extremely dexterous at solving complicated equations. By plugging electrical cords into the proper sockets of a patch panel resembling an antiquated telephone switchboard, a programmer can interconnect the various electrical components of an analog computer to represent the variables in a set of equations. When the variables are assigned values expressed as voltages, the solution emerges as another voltage that can be printed on graph paper or, as in the case of Shaw's analog computer, that can be displayed on the oscilloscope that serves as the machine's monitor.

On a January night in the basement of the Santa Cruz physics building, Shaw wired his analog computer to solve the equations that William Burke had given him. He then adjusted the controls on the monitor and settled back to see what would emerge. Within minutes, Shaw realized that he would never finish his dissertation on superconductivity; the image on the screen before him was the Lorenz attractor, as Shaw later learned it was called, being traced out in continuous motion by the glowing green blip racing across the oscilloscope.

CHAOS ON TAP

With three fellow physics students—James Crutchfield, Doyne Farmer, and Norman Packard—Shaw set out to learn everything he could about the burgeoning science of chaos. The group found evidence of chaotic behavior everywhere they looked: in the fluttering of flags, in the plume of smoke rising decorously from a cigarette only to break into disordered curlicues, in the human body's immunological defenses. Even a simple physical system like a dripping faucet becomes chaotic. As the valve in a faucet is slowly opened, water at first drips at steady, predictable intervals. But as the flow increases, Shaw observed, the drips begin to fall in an irregular and unpredictable succession.

To explore this everyday phenomenon, Shaw and faculty member Peter Scott set up an experiment in which drops from a faucet interrupted a beam of light aimed at a photodetector. A digital microcomputer was connected to the photodetector so that the computer could time the often-tiny differences in the intervals that elapsed between drops. This information was then stored on a magnetic disk for later analysis by a more sophisticated computer.

Shaw, Scott, and their colleagues were interested in divining much more than just the mechanics of a particular physical system. They wanted to establish the feasibility of devising a computer model based on observations of the system's actual behavior, rather than building the model from equations that described the system's idealized functioning. Following this route, the group believed, might help them to identify the principles underlying the faucet's unruly conduct.

To derive a graphic image of the order behind the faucet's chaotic flow, Shaw and Crutchfield set about plotting a three-dimensional graph of successive triplets of the intervals between water drops. The image that resulted showed the intervals clustered together in a decidedly nonrandom shape resembling a saxophone floating in space *(page 111)*. The two physicists also solved on the analog computer a set of three equations suggested by the dynamics of dripping water. When they compared their empirical and theoretical results, their instinct was proved correct; both approaches produced similarly shaped saxophones.

Since the mid-1980s, a growing number of mathematicians, physicists, and biologists have adapted the Santa Cruz group's "reconstruction" technique of working backward from empirical data to a behavioral model. The transition from a healthily beating heart to one fluttering on the verge of cardiac arrest, it has been found, closely parallels the transition of other systems from order to chaos. Similar findings have indicated that the rise and fall of wildlife populations and the spread of an epidemic may follow a chaotic evolution. Chaos theory has been used to study the reliability of computers, the incidence of earthquakes, the structure of lungs and blood vessels, even the movement of freeway traffic.

The common element in all of these investigations has been computers. Only with their assistance could scientists have gathered and analyzed the masses of data that were needed to understand chaotic systems, and only computers could have solved the complex equations that capture their essence. That computers have shown many phenomena to be inherently unpredictable may seem discouraging at first, but there is a brighter side. Knowing that there are limits to accurately projecting the weather, for example, can save meteorologists time and money that would have been wasted in pursuit of unachievable precision in forecasting. Chaos may even enlighten philosophers, who have argued for centuries whether there is freedom of action in the universe or whether every event is dictated in the minutest detail by circumstances. This new branch of science seems to suggest that virtually anything can happen—within limits that have yet to be established. Or, as one scientist has remarked, the universe may well be predictable, but only God knows the initial conditions.

Understanding the Unpredictable

Until recently, scientists have gone about their business secure in the belief that, beyond the subatomic world where chance reigns supreme, any event can be predicted, as long as the laws that govern the event are known and measurements can be taken to establish a starting point to which the laws can be applied. If a prediction misses the mark, the blame lies with incorrectly stated laws or imprecise measurements. Even systems that seem to defy prediction do so only because not enough is known of them—or so science always assumed.

As it turns out, nothing could be further from the truth. Since the early 1960s, scientists and mathematicians have proved that many phenomena—the weather, the electrical impulses of a heart, the progress of epidemics, a leaf falling from a tree, to name just a few—are inherently unpredictable more than a short distance into the future. The most minuscule inaccuracies in measurements at the starting point result not in sufferable errors, but in wildly gyrating behavior that mocks the very foundations of science.

The realization that much of the future is unknowable has been called the third revolutionary scientific development of the twentieth century, after relativity and quantum mechanics. The new field has been christened chaos, a name that suggests unrelieved randomness. Yet there are limits to the disorder. For example, from the perspective of January, it may be impossible to predict whether rain will fall on the Sahara in July, but there is virtually no chance that it will snow there.

To establish the boundaries of chaos, scientists depend on computers to perform the voluminous calculations necessary to evolve the future state of a system from thousands of nearly identical starting points. Because reams of computer paper printed with column upon column of figures defy human analysis, computers are also called upon to transform the abundance of data into graphs, pictures of numbers that reveal at a glance the shape and limits of chaos.

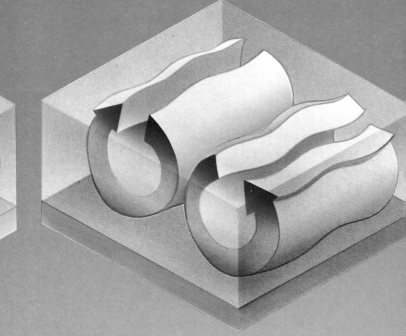

Heat applied to a fluid initially triggers cylindrical convection currents as warm fluid rises and cooler fluid descends *(above, left)*. Increasing the temperature *(above, right)* results in a prechaotic condition in which the currents become less uniform and reverse direction. During this stage the changes in flow are predictable, but with more heat, the currents eventually begin to behave in a chaotic fashion, wobbling and reversing direction capriciously *(far right)*.

The Crisis Route to Chaos

The frustrations of weather forecasting can be appreciated in the outcome of a simple computer model devised in 1962 by Edward N. Lorenz, a meteorologist at the Massachusetts Institute of Technology. The model, known as the Lorenz system, described the movements of a fluid as it is heated. Because physicists consider both liquids and gases to be fluids, the Lorenz model represents equally well a pot of water set on the stove to boil and the sun-heated sea of air that envelops the planet.

Lorenz developed his model in an effort to learn from a simple system why a complex one like the earth's weather is so unyielding to reason. Using well-understood equations of fluid dynamics, the science of liquids and gases in motion, the meteorologist found that within his model the behavior of

convection currents that form as warm fluid rises and cool fluid descends was indeed predictable—up to a point.

But as demonstrated on these pages, when the fluid became hot enough—about twenty-four times the temperature at which convection began—the model went haywire. At this temperature, an example of what scientists studying chaos call a crisis point, tried-and-true laws of fluid dynamics suddenly became inapplicable. Lorenz could no more predict the speed and direction of the convection currents than he could forecast the weather in Peoria a month in advance. The Lorenz system proved that chaos lurks even in simple systems, including many that scientists had thought completely predictable if only enough data about them could be collected and analyzed.

The onset of chaos is shown in a graph that plots the difference in temperature between ascending and descending parts of the currents, a measure of the strength of the convection. Early in the experiment, at the left of the graph, the trace is orderly. But as fluid temperature increases, the trace abruptly becomes chaotic, with no discernible pattern.

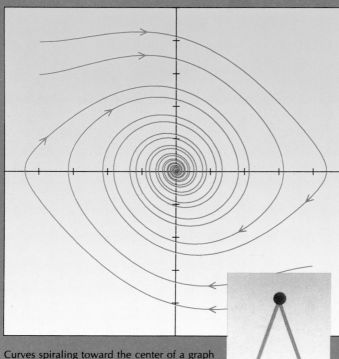

Curves spiraling toward the center of a graph plot the speed of a freely swinging pendulum against its distance to the right or left of vertical. From different starting points (four of them here), the pendulum invariably comes to rest hanging vertically, a state represented by the point attractor *(red dot)* at the center.

A limit-cycle attractor, the red loop in the diagram above, describes the steady motion of a clock pendulum, which gets a kick from the escapement on every swing. Given a soft push or a forceful one to get started, the pendulum soon settles into a repeating, predictable pattern of motion.

The three-dimensional Lorenz attractor, shown here as a somewhat idealized masklike surface, illustrates the order that underlies chaotic behavior of the Lorenz convection system. The loops, infinite in number, never intersect or repeat as they ultimately fill the shape.

Limits of Disorder

Turning down the heat under the Lorenz system settles it into a predictable pattern of motion. At a low setting, for example, the cylindrical convection currents acquire a speed and direction that remains constant as long as the temperature of the fluid is unchanged. Physicists call this kind of equilibrium an attractor. If the fluid were heated to a chaotic state and then cooled back down to the original temperature, the convection currents would resume the speed and direction they started with.

Recognized long before chaos became a topic of scientific interest, attractors range from simple to extraordinarily complex, depending on the number of variables involved. A pair of attractors for two-variable systems—a point attractor for a freely swinging pendulum and a so-called limit-cycle attractor for a clock pendulum—are explained above.

A system that exhibits truly random behavior can have no attractor, since the state of affairs at one instant is unrelated to conditions at any other instant. Plotting a graph of conditions at every instant would yield not a shape, as in the examples above, but a formless array of evenly distributed dots. When Lorenz programmed a computer to plot conditions within his model after it had passed the crisis point into chaos, he expected just this result. He was astonished to see, instead of an unstructured pointillism on the computer screen, an attractor having the spectacular pattern of loops shown at right. Lorenz's attractor was the first of a new kind now called strange attractors. The discovery established that there is order in chaos, that conditions within a system must lie on an attractor even though it may be impossible to predict precisely where.

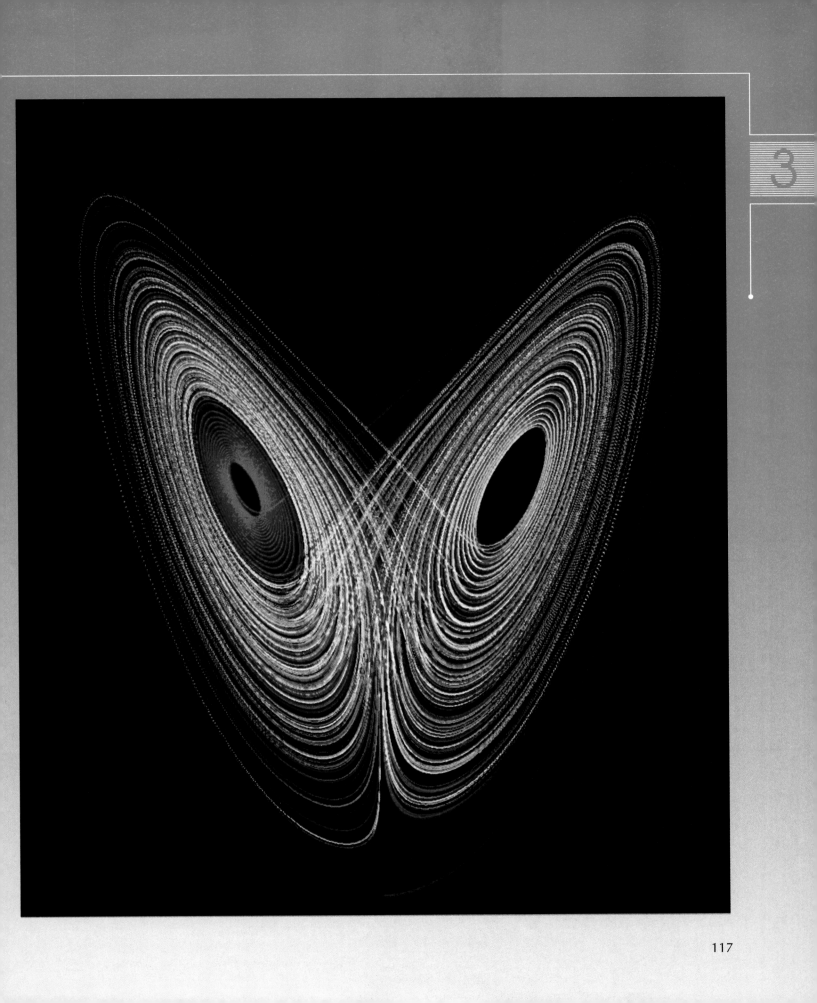

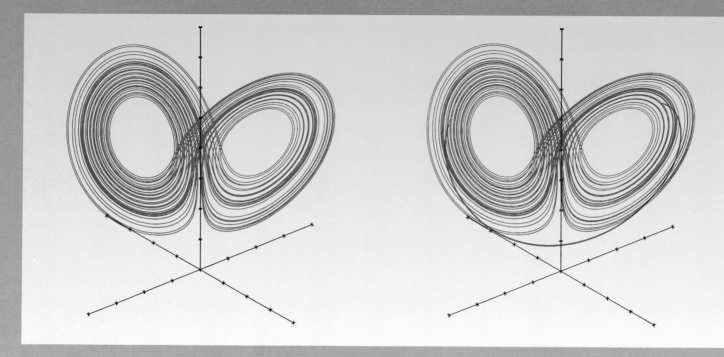

The blue disk on the attractor above, at left, contains 10,000 individual points, all falling within the margins for error of determining the position of just one point. As events unfold from left to right in the four illustrations above, the points follow their own paths, which quickly diverge.

Small Errors, Large Consequences

Scientists studying chaotic systems have learned that their capricious behavior occurs simply because, at any instant, it is impossible to know the state of such a system with sufficient accuracy to predict its future. Edward Lorenz stumbled across this feature of chaos after running a computer model of the weather. Seeking to repeat the final stages of the experiment, he restarted the model using results from midway through the first run. It happened that he rounded the values of these figures from the six significant figures of the original run to just three. A temperature of, say, 65.4271 degrees, for example, became 65.4 degrees, an error of only about twenty-seven thousandths of a degree. Expecting to see a correspondingly insignificant difference in the outcomes of the two runs, Lorenz was astonished to find that the results of the second run were utterly unlike those of the first.

The divergence developed from a phenomenon that is known among scientists as sensitivity to initial conditions.

That is, even tiny disparities in starting points, such as the small disagreement between the two sets of values that Lorenz's weather model acted upon, yield wildly different results. Taking careful measurements is no solution. A variance in the hundredth decimal place, or even in the thousandth, rapidly advances a chaotic system to an unforeseeable location on its attractor.

The computer-generated illustrations on these pages show how points representing nearly identical states of a Lorenz system are soon dispersed throughout the three-dimensional surface of the attractor. The phenomenon can be seen in processes as mundane as stirring a drop of food color into a batch of frosting for a cake. With a few strokes of a spoon, molecules of the dye, initially so close together that determining the distances between them would tax the most sophisticated of measuring devices, are dispersed far and wide throughout the mixture.

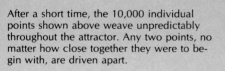

After a short time, the 10,000 individual points shown above weave unpredictably throughout the attractor. Any two points, no matter how close together they were to begin with, are driven apart.

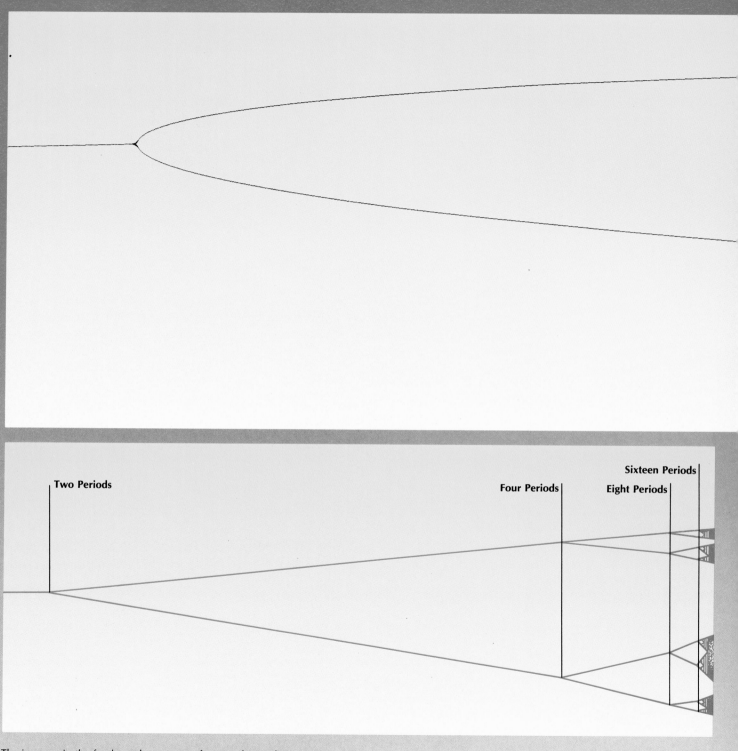

Two Periods

Four Periods

Eight Periods

Sixteen Periods

The increase in the food supply necessary for a moth population to advance from two possible values to four is 4.669 times the growth required to progress from four values to eight. This ratio, called the Feigenbaum constant after its discoverer, applies to the increase in food supply needed for further doublings in this system. It also pertains to all systems that period double to chaos, suggesting a long-obscured foundation of mathematical order in the cosmos.

Doubling and Redoubling to Chaos

Simpler systems than Lorenz's abstraction of the weather have been found to become chaotic. Indeed, systems having just a single variable can become thoroughly unpredictable, complete with a distinctive form of attractor.

The computer-generated graph above, called a bifurcation diagram, is typical of this kind of attractor. Though this example derives from no system in particular, it illustrates a route to chaos called period doubling that is found in such phenomena as the variation in an insect population—gypsy moths, for example—in response to an increase in the creatures' food supply.

The single line at the far left of the graph represents a stable situation in which, for a given availability of food, the number of moths remains constant from year to year. If the food supply increases, so does the moth population—until the line splits. To the right of this point, the number of moths alternates

from year to year between a high value and a low one as the moths outgrow the food supply and then die back, only to resurge to the higher, unsustainable value. With additional increases in the food supply, the population settles on one of four values, then eight, then sixteen, and then—chaos. Within limits defined by the attractor, the moth population can assume any value.

A bifurcation diagram has a number of interesting features. Shadowy curves indicate insect populations that are slightly more probable than others. Amid the chaos, windows of order occasionally appear in which the system reverts to period doubling. Most intriguing, however, is the discovery by mathematician Mitchell Feigenbaum that the pace at which period doubling advances from two to four to eight is identical for any system—biological, mathematical, sociological—that takes this route to chaos *(left)*.

Bibliography

Books

Abrams, M. H., ed., *The Norton Anthology of English Literature*. 2 vols. New York: W. W. Norton, 1968.

Bass, Thomas A., *The Eudaemonic Pie*. Boston: Houghton Mifflin, 1985.

Beckmann, Petr, *A History of Pi*. Boulder, Colo.: Golem, 1977.

Bertin, Eugene P., *Principles and Practice of X-Ray Spectrometric Analysis*. 2d ed. New York: Plenum Press, 1975.

Breit, William, and Roger W. Spencer, eds., *Lives of the Laureates: Seven Nobel Economists*. Cambridge: MIT Press, 1988.

Damon, S. Foster, *William Blake: His Philosophy and Symbols*. Boston: Houghton Mifflin, 1924.

Davis, Philip J., and Reuben Hersh, *The Mathematical Experience*. Boston: Birkhauser, 1981.

Dewdney, A. K., *The Armchair Universe: An Exploration of Computer Worlds*. New York: W. H. Freeman, 1988.

Erdman, David V., ed., *The Poetry and Prose of William Blake*. Garden City, N.Y.: Doubleday, 1965.

Fogel, Robert William, and Stanley L. Engerman, *Time on the Cross*. Boston: Little, Brown, 1974.

Forrester, Jay W., *World Dynamics*. Cambridge, Mass.: Wright-Allen Press, 1973.

Fuson, Robert H., *The Log of Christopher Columbus*. Camden, Maine: International Marine Publishing Co., 1987.

Garey, Michael R., and David S. Johnson, *Computers and Intractability*. San Francisco: W. H. Freeman, 1979.

Gleick, James, *Chaos: Making a New Science*. New York: Viking, 1987.

Greenberger, Martin, Matthew A. Crenson, and Brian L. Crissey, *Models in the Policy Process: Public Decision Making in the Computer Era*. New York: Russell Sage Foundation, 1976.

Halsema-Kubes, W., G. Lemmens, and G. de Werd, *Adriaen van Wesel: een Utrechtse Beeldhouwer uit de Late Middeleeuwen*. The Hague: Staatsuitgeverij, 1980.

Hardy, G. H., *A Mathematician's Apology*. Cambridge: Cambridge University Press, 1967.

Henisz-Dostert, Bozena, R. Ross Macdonald, and Michael Zarechnak, *Machine Translation*. New York: Mouton, 1978.

Hockey, Susan, *A Guide to Computer Applications in the Humanities*. London: Gerald Duckworth, 1980.

Hoffman, Paul, *Archimedes' Revenge: The Joys and Perils of Mathematics*. New York: W. W. Norton, 1988.

Hutchins, W. J., *Machine Translation: Past, Present, Future*. New York: Wiley, 1986.

Knuth, Donald, *Searching and Sorting*. Vol. 3 of *The Art of Computer Programming*. Reading, Mass.: Addison-Wesley, 1975.

Lawler, E. L., et al., eds., *The Traveling Salesman Problem*. New York: Wiley, 1985.

McCorduck, Pamela, *The Universal Machine*. New York: McGraw-Hill, 1985.

Mandelbrot, Benoit B., *The Fractal Geometry of Nature*. New York: W. H. Freeman, 1987.

Meadows, D. H., and J. M. Robinson, *The Electronic Oracle: Computer Models and Social Decisions*. New York: Wiley, 1985.

Meadows, Donella H., et al.:
Groping in the Dark: The First Decade of Global Modeling. New York: Wiley, 1982.
The Limits to Growth. New York: Universe Books, 1974.

Mosteller, Frederick, and David L. Wallace, *Inference and Disputed Authorship: The Federalist*. Reading, Mass.: Addison-Wesley, 1964.

Nirenburg, Sergei, ed., *Machine Translation*. Cambridge: Cambridge University Press, 1987.

Oakman, Robert L., *Computer Methods for Literary Research*. Athens, Ga.: University of Georgia Press, 1984.

Peitgen, Heinz-Otto, and Peter H. Richter, *The Beauty of Fractals*. Berlin: Springer-Verlag, 1986.

Shaw, Robert, *The Dripping Faucet as a Model Chaotic System*. Santa Cruz, Calif.: Ariel Press, 1984.

Shorter, Edward, *The Historian and the Computer*. Englewood Cliffs, N.J.: Prentice-Hall, 1971.

Wasson, Tyler, ed., *Nobel Prize Winners: An H. W. Wilson Biographical Dictionary*. New York: H. W. Wilson, 1987.

Periodicals

Arenson, Karen W., "Otto Eckstein: Educator Who Led in Economic Forecasting." *New York Times*, Mar. 23, 1984.

Ascher, William, "The Forecasting Potential of Complex Models." *Policy Sciences*, Vol. 13, No. 1, 1981.

Asmus, John F., "Computer Enhancement of the Mona Lisa." *Perspectives in Computing*, spring 1987.

Beard, Jonathan, "Repealing the Right to Wrinkle." *Discover*, Jan. 1988.

Begley, Sharon, "Finding Order in Disorder." *Newsweek*, Dec. 21, 1987.

Bendt, Douglas L., and Carolyne E. Lochhead, "The Economist's New Clothes." *Fortune*, Apr. 1, 1985.

"Bible Labor of Years Is Done in 400 Hours." *Life*, Feb. 11, 1957.

Borwein, Jonathan M., and Peter B. Borwein, "Ramanujan and Pi." *Scientific American*, Feb. 1988.

Brunner, Theodore F., "Data Banks for the Humanities: Learning from Thesaurus Linguae Graecae." *Scholarly Communication*, winter 1987.

Bullough, Vern L., "The Computer and the Historian—Some Tentative Beginnings." *Computers and the Humanities*, Vol. 1, 1966.

Burgess, John, " 'Modeling' Results in Elaborate Simulations of Objects, Processes." *Washington Post*, Apr. 24, 1988.

Burton, D. M., "Automated Concordances and Word Indexes." *Computers and the Humanities*, Vol. 15, 1981.

Busa, R., "The Annals of Humanities Computing: The Index Thomisticus." *Computers and the Humanities*, Vol. 14, 1980.

Bush, Vannevar, "As We May Think." *Atlantic Monthly*, July 1945.

Campbell, Colin, "Use of Computer as Literary Tool Gains." *New York Times*, Aug. 2, 1984.

Campbell, David, et al., "Experimental Mathematics: The Role of Computation in Nonlinear Science." *Communications of the ACM*, Apr. 1985.

Clubb, Jerome M., "Computer Technology and the Source Materials of Social Science History." *Social Science History*, summer 1986.

Comer, Douglas, "The Ubiquitous B-Tree." *Computing Surveys*, June 1979.

Crawford, David J., "Computing Pi." *BYTE*, May 1985.

Crutchfield, James P., et al., "Chaos." *Scientific American*, Dec. 1986.

Dibble, Harold, "Measurement of Artifact Provenience with an Electronic Theodolite." *Journal of Field Archaeology*, Vol. 14, 1987.

Edelson, Edward, "The Problem of Macrovariables." *Mosaic*, spring 1986.

Fair, Ray C., "Macroeconomics in the Classroom—No Longer

Just Theory." *Perspectives in Computing,* summer 1985.

Fillieres, Dominique, et al., "Neutron-Activation Study of Figurines, Pottery, and Workshop Materials from the Athenian Agora, Greece." *Journal of Field Archaeology,* Vol. 10, 1983.

Fisher, Arthur, "Chaos: The Ultimate Asymmetry." *Mosaic,* Jan./Feb. 1985.

Forrester, Jay W.:

"Counterintuitive Behavior of Social Systems." *Technology Review,* Jan. 1971.

"Lessons from System Dynamics Modeling." *System Dynamics Review,* Vol. 3, No. 2.

Freifeld, Karen, "Art Analysis: Probing beneath the Image." *IEEE Spectrum,* June 1986.

Gleick, James:

"Even with Action Today, Ozone Loss Will Increase." *New York Times,* Mar. 20, 1988.

"An Isolated Genius Is Given His Due." *New York Times,* July 14, 1987.

Goldberg, R. A., G. Tisnado M., and R. A. Scofield, "Characteristics of Extreme Rainfall Events in Northwestern Peru during the 1982-1983 El Niño Period." *Journal of Geophysical Research,* Dec. 15, 1987.

Gray, J. C., "Creating the Electronic New Oxford English Dictionary." *Computers and the Humanities,* Vol. 20, 1986.

Helgerson, Linda, "Scanners Present Maze of Options." *Mini-Micro Systems,* Jan. 1987.

Heppenheimer, T. A., "Machines That Read." *Popular Science,* Mar. 1987.

Horgan, John, "But Is It Art?" *Scientific American,* Oct. 1987.

Houston, Tom R., "Why Models Go Wrong." *BYTE,* Oct. 1985.

Hughes, John J., "From Homer to Hesychius—the Thesaurus Linguae Graecae Project." *Bits and Bytes Review,* June 1987.

Imhof, Arthur E., "The Computer in Social History: Historical Demography in Germany." *Computers and the Humanities,* Vol. 12, 1978.

Jantz, Richard, "The 300-Word-per-Minute Typist." *Publish!,* Apr. 1988.

Jensen, Richard, "The Microcomputer Revolution for Historians." *Journal of Interdisciplinary History,* summer 1983.

Judge, Joseph, "Where Columbus Found the New World." *National Geographic,* Nov. 1986.

Karp, Richard M., "Combinatorics, Complexity, and Randomness." *Communications of the ACM,* Feb. 1986.

Kerr, Richard A., "Stratospheric Ozone Is Decreasing." *Science,* Mar. 25, 1988.

Kiehl, J. T., et al., "Response of a General Circulation Model to a Prescribed Antarctic Ozone Hole." *Nature,* Apr. 7, 1988.

King, M., and S. Perschke, "EUROTRA and Its Objectives." *Multilingua,* 1982.

Klein, Lawrence R., et al., "The World Economy—A Global Model." *Perspectives in Computing,* May 1982.

Kolata, Gina:

"Asking Impossible Questions about the Economy and Getting Impossible Answers." *Science,* Oct. 31, 1986.

"Shakespeare's New Poem: An Ode to Statistics." *Science,* Jan. 24, 1986.

"Trial-and-Error Games That Puzzle Fast Computers." *Smithsonian,* Oct. 1979.

Lehmann, Winfred P., "The Context of Machine Translation." *Computers and Translation,* July-Sept. 1987.

Leontief, Wassily, Faye Duchin, and Daniel B. Szyld, "New Approaches in Economic Analysis." *Science,* Apr. 26, 1985.

Lin, S., and B. W. Kernighan, "An Effective Algorithm for the Traveling Salesman Problem." *Operations Research,* Mar./Apr. 1973.

Lorenz, Edward N., "Deterministic Nonperiodic Flow." *Journal of the Atmospheric Sciences,* Mar. 1963.

Lowenstein, Frank, "Seasons, Seas, and Satellites." *Air & Space,* Feb./Mar. 1988.

McDermott, Jeanne, "Geometrical Forms Known as Fractals Find Sense in Chaos." *Smithsonian,* Dec. 1983.

McWilliams, Gary, "Economic Modeling Gains despite Accuracy Concerns." *Datamation,* Apr. 1, 1988.

Madry, Scott L. H., "Remote Sensing in Archaeology." *Archaeology,* May/June 1983.

Malley, Deborah DeWitt, "Lawrence Klein and His Forecasting Machine." *Fortune,* Mar. 1975.

Mansell, Darrel, "The Old Man and the Sea and the Computer." *Computers and the Humanities,* Vol. 8, 1974.

Marchionini, Gary, and Ben Shneiderman, "Finding Facts vs. Browsing Knowledge in Hypertext Systems." *Computer,* Jan. 1988.

Marden, Luis, "Columbus and the New World: Tracking Columbus across the Atlantic." *National Geographic,* Nov. 1986.

Meadows, Donella H., "Charting the Way the World Works." *Technology Review,* Feb./Mar. 1985.

Miller, David W., "The Computer's Place in Historical Research." *AHA Newsletter,* Vol. 20, No. 1.

Miller, David W., and John Modell, "Teaching U.S. History with the Great American History Machine." *Historical Methods,* summer 1988.

"New Tools Are Aiding Excavation of Sites." *New York Times,* Mar. 1, 1988.

Peterson, Cass, "Evidence of Ozone Depletion Found over Big Urban Areas." *Washington Post,* Mar. 16, 1988.

Peterson, Ivars:

"Millions of Digits of Pi." *Science News,* Feb. 8, 1986.

"Pi Wars: Dueling Supercomputers." *Science News,* Feb. 21, 1987.

"The Practical Fractal." *The Economist,* Dec. 26, 1987.

Raben, Joseph, "Computer Applications in the Humanities." *Science,* Apr. 26, 1985.

Rodgers, Clive, "Global Ozone Trends Reassessed." *Nature,* Mar. 17, 1988.

Rowland, Sherwood, "Can We Close the Ozone Hole?" *Technology Review,* Aug./Sept. 1987.

Rowney, Don Karl, "The Historian and the Microcomputer." *BYTE,* July 1982.

Schick, James B. M., "Historians and Computing, circa 1987." *Social Science Microcomputer Review,* winter 1987.

Schoenbaum, S., "Marvin Spevack, 'A Complete and Systematic Concordance to the Works of Shakespeare.'" *Computers and the Humanities,* Sept. 1971.

Shabecoff, Philip:

"Industry Acts to Curb Peril in Ozone Loss." *New York Times,* Mar. 21, 1988.

"Study Shows Significant Decline in Ozone Layer." *New York Times,* Mar. 16, 1988.

Shell, Ellen Ruppel, "Solo Flights into the Ozone Hole Reveal Its Causes." *Smithsonian,* Feb. 1988.

Shiller, Robert J., "Economic Forecasting." *New York Times,* Apr. 7, 1981.

Shurkin, Joel N., "Exploring Chaos." *Christian Science Monitor,* Sept. 9, 1986.

Stephen, V. M., and Douglas B. Craig, "Recovering the Past Bit by Bit with Microcomputers." *Archaeology,* July/Aug. 1984.

Stolarski, Richard, "The Antarctic Ozone Hole." *Scientific American,* Jan. 1988.

Sullivan, Walter, "Space-Age Methods Penetrate Art of the Past." *Science Times, New York Times,* June 17, 1986.

Swierenga, Robert P., "Clio and Computers: A Survey of Computerized Research in History." *Computers and the Humanities,* Sept. 1970.

Tankard, Jim, "The Literary Detective." *BYTE,* Feb. 1986.

Taubes, Gary, "The Mathematics of Chaos." *Discover,* Sept. 1984.

Tucker, Allen B., Jr., "A Perspective on Machine Translation: Theory and Practice." *Communications of the ACM,* Apr. 1984.

Uchitelle, Louis, "The Shift in Forecasting." *New York Times,* July 15, 1987.

Weisburd, Stefi:
"The Art Detectives." *Science News,* Apr. 23, 1988.
"Ozone Reports Stir Debate." *Science News,* Jan. 9, 1988.

Weisskopf, Michael, "CFCs: Rise and Fall of Chemical Miracle." *Washington Post,* Apr. 10, 1988.

"Wharton's Swiss Parent Buys Chase Econometrics." *Wall Street Journal,* Apr. 2, 1987.

Woods, Robert L., Jr., "Historians, Programmers, and Computer Languages." *Computers and the Humanities,* 1982.

Yankelovich, Nicole, George P. Landow, and David Cody, "Creating Hypermedia Materials for English Literature Students." *SIGCUE,* Vol. 20, 1987.

Zarechnak, Michael, "Space Age and Machine Translation." *DIR,* Nov. 1987.

Other Sources

Berg, Donna Lee, et al., *The New Oxford English Dictionary Project at the University of Waterloo.* Waterloo, Ontario: UW Centre for the New Oxford English Dictionary, Feb. 1988.

Busa, Roberto, "Concordances." In *Encyclopedia of Library and Information Services.* New York: Marcel Dekker, 1974.

Calmes, Alan R., and Edward A. Miller, "Registration and Comparison of Electronic Images Obtained at Different Times for Aging Studies of the U.S. Constitution."

Cassidy, Frederic G., "Some Uses of Computers in Lexicography—the DARE Experience." In *Data Bases in the Humanities and Social Sciences.* Amsterdam: North-Holland Publishing Co., 1980.

"Columbus Research Tool: Project Summary." Control Data Corp., Minneapolis, Minn., Aug. 7, 1986.

Conklin, Jeff, "A Survey of Hypertext." MCC Technical Report STP-356-86, Rev. 2, Dec. 3, 1987.

Evans, Michael K., and Lawrence R. Klein, *The Wharton Econometric Forecasting Model.* Philadelphia: Economics Research Unit, University of Pennsylvania, 1968.

Executive Summary of the Ozone Trends Panel, Mar. 15, 1988. NASA Headquarters, Washington, D.C.

Francis, Ivor S., "An Exposition of a Statistical Approach to the Federalist Dispute." In *The Computer and Literary Style.* Kent, Ohio: Kent State University Press, 1965.

Greenhouse Consultants, Inc., *Project Report.* Oct., 1985.

Gunn, Joel, "Computers in Field Archaeology." Unpublished ms. Center for Archaeological Research, San Antonio, Tex.

Kevex Corporation, *X-Ray Fluorescence and the Conservation Industry,* May 1986.

Kvamme, Kenneth L., "The Use of Geographic Information Systems for Modeling Archaeological Site Distributions." In *Geographic Information Systems in Government.* Hampton, Va.: A. Deepak, 1986.

Lillestrand, R. L., "Columbus Research Tool." Unpublished paper. Control Data Corp., Minneapolis, Minn., Sept. 8, 1986.

Stern, Randall, "The Technology behind DISCOVER." Cambridge, Mass.: Kurzweil Computer Products.

Tinbergen, J., *A Method and Its Application to Investment Activity.* Geneva: League of Nations Economic Intelligence Service, 1939.

Treinish, Lloyd A., "An Interactive, Discipline-Independent Data Visualization System." NASA, Goddard Space Flight Center, Mar. 1988.

Wecksung, George, et al., "Infrared Reflectogram Assembly by Digital Image Processing." In *American Institute for Conservation of Historic and Artistic Works: Preprints,* May 1987.

Wheeler, Peter J., "SYSTRAN." In *Machine Translation Today: The State of the Art.* Proceedings of the Third Lugano Tutorial, Lugano, Switzerland, Apr. 2-7, 1984. Edinburgh University Press, 1984.

Woiceshyn, Peter, "The Meteorology of the Pacific Ocean as Seen by Seasat on Sept. 7th, 1978 at Approximately 0600 GMT with the Scatterometer." Draft of unpublished article.

Picture Credits

H. Borwein, *Scientific American*, February 1988. 35: John Moss/ Colorific!, London, courtesy of The Royal Society of London from "Ramanujan and Pi" by Jonathan M. Borwein and Peter H. Borwein, *Scientific American*, pp.112-117, February 1988. 37: Detail of digitized Mona Lisa, John F. Asmus, University of California, San Diego, and Ralph Bernstein, IBM Palo Alto Scientific Center. 38, 39: Art by Douglas R. Chezem; National Archives—computer-screen photos by Larry Sherer, courtesy The National Archives. Background, National Archives. 40, 41: The Metropolitan Museum of Art, Rogers Fund, 1916 (16.69), photographed by Geoffrey Clements, New York, except art by Douglas R. Chezem. 42, 43: Réunion des Musées Nationaux, Paris/Musée du Louvre, Paris (4); John F. Asmus, University of California, San Diego, and Ralph Bernstein, IBM Palo Alto Scientific Center (2). Background, Réunion des Musées Nationaux, Paris/Musée du Louvre, Paris. 44, 45: Staatliche Museen zu Berlin, Skulpturensammlung, DDR, except chart by John Drummond. 46, 47: Art by Douglas R. Chezem; National Gallery of Art, Andrew Mellon Collection; computer-screen photos, Michael Latil, courtesy Kevex Corporation and The National Gallery of Art. Background, National Gallery of Art. 48: Art by Douglas R. Chezem—American School of Classical Studies at Athens: Agora Excavations (3). Background, Giraudon/Art Resource. 49: Chart by Robert K. Herndon. 50: Art by Stephen R. Wagner. 52, 53: Art by Stephen R. Wagner, copied by Larry Sherer. 54-57: Art by Al Kettler. 58: David Lees, Florence, courtesy of Professor Roberto Busa, S.J. 60-63: Art by Stephen R. Wagner, copied by Larry Sherer. 64, 65: Art by Alvin Pagan. 68: Art by Douglas R. Chezem. 69-71: Art by John Drummond. 72: Art by Robert K. Herndon—art by John Drummond. 73: Art by John Drummond. 74-77: Art by Stephen R. Wagner, copied by Larry Sherer. 78-83: Art by Stephen R. Wagner. 84, 85: Art by Stephen R. Wagner; Fitzwilliam Museum, Cambridge. 86-89: Art by Stephen R. Wagner. 90, 91: National Portrait Gallery, London; The National Trust Photographic Library, London—The Tate Gallery, London. Background art by Stephen R. Wagner. 92-99: Art by Stephen R. Wagner. 100-103: Art Matrix/The Cornell Supercomputer Facility. 105-107: Art by Stephen R. Wagner. 109: Richard Wood. 111: Yoav/Phototake. 113: Chart by Tina Taylor. 114, 115: Art by Matt McMullen—graph by Tina Taylor. 116: Charts by Dr. James P. Crutchfield—art by Matt McMullen. 117: Art Matrix/Cornell Supercomputer Facility. 118, 119: Dr. James P. Crutchfield. 120, 121: James A. Yorke/Institute for Physical Science and Technology—line art by Tina Taylor.

Acknowledgments

The editors wish to thank: **In Canada:** Montreal—Leon Glass, McGill University; Toronto—Barron Brainerd, University of Toronto; Waterloo—Donna Lee Berg and William Pulleyblank, University of Waterloo. **In East Germany:** Berlin—Michael Knuth and Lothar Lambacher, Staatliche Museen zu Berlin. **In England:** Oxford—Robert May, Oxford University. **In France:** Paris—Christian Lahanier, Laboratoire de Recherche des Musées de France. **In Italy:** Gallarate—Roberto Busa, S.J.; Rome—Graeme Barker and Amanda Claridge, British School at Rome. **In West Germany:** Hamburg—Dieter Eckstein and Peter Klein, Universität Hamburg. **In the United States:** Arizona—Tempe: Sylvia Gaines, Arizona State University; Tucson: Kenneth Kvamme, University of Arizona; Arkansas—Fayetteville: Jim Farley, Arkansas Archaeological Survey; California—Berkeley: Richard Karp, University of California; Hollywood: Peter Sorensen; Irvine: Theodore F. Brunner, University of California; La Jolla: John F. Asmus, University of California; Alan Portela, SYSTRAN Translation Systems, Inc.; Menlo Park: Herbert Shaw, U.S. Geological Survey; Palo Alto: Ralph Bernstein, IBM; Catherine Gordon, Dialog Information Services, Inc.; Bernardo Huberman, Xerox; Pasadena: Moustafa T. Chahine, Jean O. Dickey, Kevin J. Hussey, Edward A. Miller, Sylvie J. Rueff, and Peter M. Woiceshyn, Jet Propulsion Laboratory; San Carlos: Ken Stehr, Kevex Corporation; San Jose: Jennifer Mitchell, Data Quest; Santa Clara: Joan Haber, Palantir Corporation; Colorado—Boulder: John Gille and Stephen Schneider, NCAR; Connecticut—Danbury: Michael F. Marchionna, Perkin Elmer; Milford: Jack Butler, IBM; New Haven: Ray Fair, Cowles Foundation; District of Columbia—Patricia Eaton, Margaret Jorgensen, Gary Pasternak, and Kermit Sande, Defense Mapping Agency; Michael Zarechnak, Georgetown University; Arnold Meltzer, George Washington University; Michael Prather and Robert Watson, NASA; Alan Calmes, National Archives; Herb Schantz, National Computer Systems; Barbara Berrie, David Bull, Lisha Glinsman, and Michael Palmer, National Gallery of Art; Joseph Judge, National Geographic; Marjorie Leon, Pan American Health Organization; Ivars Peterson, *Science News;* Douglas Owsley, Smithsonian Institution; Douglas R. Hale, United States Department of Energy; Georgia—Atlanta: Barry Greenhouse, Greenhouse Consultants, Inc.; Illinois—Champaign: Robert Shaw, University of Illinois; Chicago: Robert W. Fogel, Ronald Thisted, and David Wallace, University of Chicago; Kansas—Pittsburg: James Schick, Pittsburg State University; Maryland—Baltimore: Peter Batke, Johns Hopkins University; Columbia: Eldon Ziegler, NCT; College Park: Celso Grebogi, Ed Ott, and Frank Varosi, University of Maryland; Gaithersburg: John R. Solomon, Input Solutions, Inc.; Greenbelt: Richard Stolarski and Lloyd Treinish, NASA; Kensington: Jane Gruenebaum; Rockville: Stephen Koslow and Ron Schoenfeld, National Institute of Mental Health; Silver Spring: Marilyn Courtot, Association for Information and Image Management; Suitland: Edward V. Sayre, Smithsonian Conservation Analytical Laboratory; Maine—Brunswick: Allen B. Tucker, Bowdoin College; Massachusetts—Boston: Farouk El Baz, Boston University; Lisa Black, Cone Communications; Stephen McNees, Federal Reserve Bank; Al Wesolowsky, *Journal of Field Archaeology;* Cambridge: Frederick Mosteller, Harvard University; Richard Saley, Harvard Semitic Museum; Denise Widman, Kurzweil Computer Products; Jay Forrester, John Sterman, and Ed Roberts, Massachusetts Institute of Technology; Michigan—Ann Arbor: Jerome Clubb, University of Michigan; Mississippi—Jackson: Scott Madry, Space Remote Sensing Center; New Hampshire—Hanover: Darrel Mansell, Dartmouth College; Plainfield: Dana Meadows; New Jersey—Fairfield: Ron Albeck and Dana Berzin, Ricoh Corporation; Middletown: Shen Lin, AT&T Information Systems; Murray Hill: Ronald Graham and Brian Kernighan, AT&T Bell Laboratories; Princeton: Dorothy Burr Thompson, Princeton University; Trenton: Bruce R. Herrick; New Mexico—Albuquerque: James I. Ebert, Ebert and Associates; Santa Fe: James J. Walker, Amparts Corporation; New York—Albany: Isabel Nirenberg, SUNY Albany; Amherst: Sam Cole; Armonk: Andy Russell, IBM; Ithaca: Homer Smith, Art Matrix; Lake Success: David Wells, Canon USA; Jericho: Ken Epstein, Canon USA; New York: Joe Jimenes, American Museum of Natural History; Joel W. Grossman, Grossman and Associates; Maryan Ainsworth, Metropolitan Museum of Art; Mitchell Feigenbaum, Rockefeller University; Jerry Lyons, W. H. Freeman Co.; Peggy Burnes, Warren Gorham and Lamont; Poughkeepsie: Nancy Ide; Yorktown Heights: Marc na; Tennessee—Oak Ridge: Edward Aebischer, Oak Ridge National Laboratory; Texas—Austin: Jeff Conklin and Jonathan Slocum, Microelectronics and Computer Technology Corporation; Eric Kostelich, University of Texas; Houston: Hannes Voigt, Rice University; McKinney: Joel Kolbensvik and Tim Sloan, Academic Computing; San Antonio: Joel Gunn, University of Texas; Virginia—Arlington: Gerald Barney and Brian Kreutzer, Institute for 21st Century Studies; Fairfax: James Trefil, George Mason University; Falls Church: Linda Helgerson, Diversified Data Resources; Vermont—Manchester Center: Linda Cooper, Recognition Technology Users Association; Wisconsin—Madison: Richard Askey, Frederic Cassidy, and Merle Curti, University of Wisconsin.

Auslander, Benoit Mandelbrot, Alan Norton, and Clifford Pickover, IBM; White Plains: Tim Ohsann, IBM; Ohio—Cleveland: Louis Milic, Cleveland State University; Columbus: Richard Bowers, Applied Information Technologies Research Center; Oberlin: James Helm, Oberlin College; Oregon—Beaverton: Greg Durose and Thomas Gifford, Saba Technologies; Pennsylvania—Philadelphia: John Abercombie, F. Gerard Adams, Harold L. Dibble, and Lawrence Klein, University of Pennsylvania; Pittsburgh: Bert Moore, AIM, Inc.; David Miller, Carnegie Mellon University; Rhode Island—Providence: James Voytuk, American Mathematical Society; Norman Meyrowitz and Jane Sanchez, Brown University; South Carolina—Columbia: Robert Oakman, University of South Caroli-

Index

Numerals in italics indicate an illustration of the subject mentioned.

A

Antarctica: ozone hole, *8-9*, 106-108
Aquinas, Thomas: 53, 58
Archaeology: 29-32, *33*
Archimedes: 35
Artifacts, computerized study of: 37; atomic analysis, *46-49*; dating, *44-45*; infrared art probes, *40-41*; monitoring condition, *38-39*; restoration, *42-43*
Atmosphere, general-circulation models of: 107; and chaos theory, 108
Attractors: *116-119*; bifurcation diagram, *120-121*; Lorenz, 110, 111, 116, *117*, *118-119*; strange, *111*
Authorship, analysis of: 61-62
Automatic Language Processing Advisory Committee (ALPAC): 76

B

Bailey, David: 36
Berndt, Bruce: 36
Bible: concordances, 53, *54-57*, 59-60
Binary trees: *54-57*
Blake, William: 82-89, *90*, 91
Bogue, Allan: 19
Booth, Andrew D.: 67
Borwein, Jonathan and Peter: 36
Brigham Young University: BYU Concordance Program, 60
Brookings Institution: econometric model, 96
Brown University: 83
Browser, hypermedia: *88-89*
Brunner, Theodore F.: 60
Burke, William: 110
Burroughs B5500: 97
Busa, Roberto: 53, *58-59*
Bush, Vannevar: 78-79, 90-91
Butterfly Effect: 110

C

Cassidy, Frederic G.: 66
Chaos: 110

Chaos theory: 93, 108-112, 113, *114-121*; Lorenz attractor, 110, 111, 116, *117*; and meteorology, 108-110, *114-115*; period doubling, *120-121*; sensitive dependence on initial conditions, 110, *118-119*
Chase Econometric Associates: 97, 98, 99
Chlorofluorocarbons (CFCs): and ozone layer, 105-108
Choropleth maps: 22-23
Cliometrics: 19-23
Clouds: *12-13*
Club of Rome: 104, 105
Columbus, Christopher: landfall in America, 17, 23, *24-27*, 28-29
Columbus Research Tool: 17, 23, *24-27*, 28-29
Commission of European Communities: and translation, 77
Concordances: 52-53, *54-57*, 58-60
Conrad, Alfred: 21
Control Data Corporation (CDC): 28; Cyber 170/185, 17, 28; 7600, 35
Cray-2: 36
Crutchfield, James: 111, 112
Curti, Merle: 19

D

Database searching: *64-65*
Data Resources, Inc. (DRI): 96-97, 98, 99
Defense Mapping Agency: Topographic Center, 32
Dendrochronology: *44-45*
Devitt, Scott: 28
Dibble, Harold: 30
Dictionaries: 62-63, 66
Dictionary of American Regional English (DARE): 63, 66
Digital Equipment Corporation (DEC): strategy, 104
Digitizers: 32. *See also* Optical character readers
Dostert, Leon E.: 67, 74, 75

E

Ebert, Jim: 30

Eckstein, Otto: 96-97
Econometrics: 94-99; Brookings model, 96; commercialization, 96-97, 98-99; equations, 94; limitations, 97-98; on personal computers, 98-99; practitioners, 94-97; Wharton models, 95-96
Efron, Bradley: 61
Electronic libraries: 60-61
Ellison, John W.: 59-60
Engerman, Stanley: 21
ENIAC: and pi, 35
Epson HX-20: 31
EUROTRA: 77
Evans, Michael: 95, 96, 97

F

Fair, Ray: 98
Farman, Joseph: 106-107
Farmer, Doyne: 111
Federalist Papers, The: 61
Feigenbaum, Mitchell: 120-121
Fogel, Robert: 22
Forrester, Jay: 99, 104
Fractal geometry: *100-103*
Freon: 106

G

Garvin, Paul: 74
Gauss-Seidel technique: 96
GE-635: 34
Genealogy: 20-21
Geographic Information System (GIS): 31-32
Georgetown Automatic Translation (GAT): 75
Gleick, James: 110
Global Jewish Database/Responsa Project: 60-61
Goldberger, Arthur: 95
Graphics, computer: *6-15*
Great American History Machine (GAHM): 22
Greene, Stephan: 23
Greenhouse Consultants: 30-31
Grossman, Joel W.: 30-31

H

Hamilton, Alexander: 61
Hardy, Godfrey H.: 36
Held, Michael: 33-34
Hemingway, Ernest: 51-52
Historical investigations: 18. *See also*
   Artifacts; Cliometrics
Hoffman, Paul: 32
Husky Hawk: 30
Hypermedia: *78-91;* browser, *88-89;*
   links, *84-87;* nodes, *80-81;* use, *90-91;*
   windows, *82-83*

I

IBM: 33; and concordance to Aquinas,
   58, 59; and machine translation, 74;
   704, 35
Imhof, Arthur: 20, 21
Interuniversity Consortium for Political
   and Social Research (ICPSR): 19

J

Judge, Joseph: 23, 24, 28, 29

K

Kanada, Yasumasa: 36
Karp, Richard: 33-34
Kernighan, Brian: 34
Kertesz, François: 75
Kjetsaa, Geir: 62
Klein, Lawrence: 95-96, 97, 99
Klein-Goldberger model: 95
Koenig, William: 51
Kryukov, Fyodor: 62
Kvamme, Kenneth: 32

L

LANDSAT: 32
La Quina, France: 32, *33*
Lexicography: 62-63, 66
Li, Tien-Yien: 110
Lillestrand, Robert: 28-29
Limits to Growth, The: 105
Lin, Shen: 34
Links, hypermedia: *84-85;* types, *86-87*
Literary investigations: 18, 51-77;
   authorship, 61-62; dictionaries, 62-63,
   66; style and date analysis, 51-52;
   translation, 66-67
Logos Development Corporation: 77
Lorenz, Edward N.: 108, *109*-110, 116
   118; attractor, 110, 111, *117, 118-119;*
   model, *114-115*

M

McCarthy, Joseph: 95
McGraw-Hill: 97, 99
Machine-readable texts: collections, 60
Machine translation (MT): 66-67, 74-77;
   automatic dictionary, 67, 74; program
   cutbacks, 75-76
McNees, Stephen: 93

Madison, James: 61
Madry, Scott: 32
Magnetic fields, planetary: Uranus, *14-15*
Mandelbrot, Benoit: 100
Mansell, Darrel: 51
Maps, computer-generated: 23, 28;
   choropleth, 22-23
Marden, Luis and Ethel: 28
Marron, Donald: 96
Mathematics: complexity theory, 35; pi,
   35-36; fractal geometry, *100-103;*
   traveling-salesman problem, 32-34
Meadows, Dennis and Donella: 105
Meteorology: and chaos theory, 108, *109,*
   110. *See also* Ozone layer
Meyer, John: 21
Miller, David: 20-21, 22
Modeling, computer: econometric, 93-99;
   physical systems, 105-112; system
   dynamics, 99, 104-105; uses, 93
Mona Lisa: 42-43
Morison, Samuel Eliot: 17, 23, 24
Mosteller, Frederick: 61

N

Neutron activation analysis: *48-49*
Newton, Isaac: 35
New York City: excavation, 30-31
Nimbus 7: 107
Nodes, hypermedia: *80-81*

O

Oak Ridge National Laboratory: and
   machine translation, 75
Okun, Arthur: 98
Old Man and the Sea, The: 51-52
Olsen, Kenneth: 104
Optical character readers (OCRs): *68-73;*
   expert systems, *73;* feature analysis,
   71-72, 73; matrix matching, *70, 71,*
   73
Oxford Computing Service: 60
Oxford English Dictionary: 63
Ozone layer: *8-9,* 106-108; modeling,
   107-108

P

Packard, Norman: 111
Pi: calculation of, *34, 35-36*

R

Ramanujan, Srinivasa: *35,* 36
Remington Rand: UNIVAC, 59
Richens, Richard: 67
Royal McBee: 108
Ryti, Carla: 28

S

Saltzman, Barry: 110
Satellite remote sensing: clouds, *12-13;*
   ozone, *8-9;* winds, *6-7*
Scott, Peter: 112

Shakespeare, William: 61
Shaw, Robert: 110-111
Sholokhov, Mikhail: 61-62
Shorter, Edward: 18
Shubik, Martin: 105
Silent Don, The: 61-62
Slavery in U.S.: 21-22
Spevack, Marvin: 60
Spiegel, Edward: 110
SPOT satellite: 32
Statistics: mapping, 22
System dynamics: 99, 104; business
   models, 99, 104; world model, 104
SYSTRAN: 76-77

T

Tamaya: 28
TAUM-METEO translation system: 77
Taylor, Gary: 62
Thesaurus Linguae Graecae: 60
Thisted, Ronald: 61
Time on the Cross: 21
Time-sharing: and DRI, 97; and personal
   computers, 98
Tinbergen, Jan: 93, 94
Toma, Peter: 76
Transit, infrared: 31
Translation: *See* Machine translation
Traveling-salesman problem (TSP): 32-
   34
Turner, Frederick Jackson: 19

U

United States Census: 19, 20; of slaves,
   21
United States Geological Survey: 32
UNIVAC: 59
University of Michigan: ICPSR, 19

V

Van Wesel, Adriaen: 44-45
Verhoog, Pieter: 23
Voyager: 15

W

Wallace, David: 61
Watson, Thomas J.: 59
Weather: *10-11*
Weaver, Warren: 67, 77
Wharton Econometric Forecasting
   Associates (WEFA): 97, 98, 99
Wharton School of Business, University of
   Pennsylvania: economic forecasts, 95
Wiener, Norbert: 67
Winchester, Ian: 20
Windows, hypermedia: *82-83*
Wind patterns, oceanic: *6-7*
Woods, Robert, Jr.: 18-19
Word-Cruncher: 60

X

X-ray fluorescence spectroscopy: *46-47*

Time-Life Books Inc.
is a wholly owned subsidiary of
TIME INCORPORATED

FOUNDER: Henry R. Luce 1898-1967

Editor-in-Chief: Jason McManus
Chairman and Chief Executive Officer:
J. Richard Munro
President and Chief Operating Officer:
N. J. Nicholas, Jr.
Editorial Director: Ray Cave
Executive Vice President, Books: Kelso F. Sutton
Vice President, Books: George Artandi

TIME-LIFE BOOKS INC.

EDITOR: George Constable
Executive Editor: Ellen Phillips
Director of Design: Louis Klein
Director of Editorial Resources: Phyllis K. Wise
Editorial Board: Russell B. Adams, Jr.,
Dale M. Brown, Roberta Conlan, Thomas H.
Flaherty, Lee Hassig, Donia Ann Steele,
Rosalind Stubenberg
Director of Photography and Research:
John Conrad Weiser
Assistant Director of Editorial Resources:
Elise Ritter Gibson

PRESIDENT: Christopher T. Linen
Chief Operating Officer: John M. Fahey, Jr.
Senior Vice Presidents: Robert M. DeSena,
James L. Mercer, Paul R. Stewart
Vice Presidents: Stephen L. Bair, Ralph J. Cuomo,
Neal Goff, Stephen L. Goldstein, Juanita T. James,
Hallett Johnson III, Carol Kaplan, Susan J. Maruyama,
Robert H. Smith, Joseph J. Ward
Director of Production Services: Robert J. Passantino

Editorial Operations
Copy Chief: Diane Ullius
Production: Celia Beattie
Library: Louise D. Forstall

Correspondents: Elisabeth Kraemer-Singh (Bonn);
Maria Vincenza Aloisi, (Paris); Ann Natanson (Rome).
Valuable assistance was also provided by: Saskia van
de Linde (Amsterdam); Mirka Gondicas (Athens);
Angie Lemmer (Bonn); Vanessa Kramer and Christine
Hinze (London); Trini Bandres (Madrid);
Elizabeth Brown and Christina Lieberman (New York);
Ann Wise (Rome).

UNDERSTANDING COMPUTERS

SERIES DIRECTOR: Lee Hassig
Series Administrator: Loretta Britten

Editorial Staff for *The Puzzle Master*
Designer: Robert K. Herndon
Associate Editors: Kristin Baker (pictures),
Allan Fallow, Margery A. duMond (text)
Researchers: Steven Feldman, Flora J. Garcia, Tucker
Jones, Laura E. Trivers
Writer: Robert M. S. Somerville
Assistant Designer: Sue Deal-Daniels
Copy Coordinator: Elizabeth Graham
Picture Coordinator: Robert H. Wooldridge, Jr.
Editorial Assistant: Susan L. Finken

Special Contributors: Elisabeth Carpenter, Carol Eron,
Richard Jenkins, Martin Mann, Steve Olson, Eugene
Rodgers, Joseph Raben, John Rubin (text); Edward Dix-
on, Gregory A. McGruder, Pamela L. Whitney, (research); Mel Ingber (index)

THE CONSULTANTS

PETER BORWEIN is a professor of mathematics at Dalhousie University in Halifax, Nova Scotia. He has been
investigating the computation of pi since 1983.

JAMES CRUTCHFIELD is a research physicist at the University of California at Berkeley, where he is studying the
structure underlying complexity.

J. DOYNE FARMER is leader of the complex-systems
group in the theoretical division of Los Alamos National
Laboratory, New Mexico.

LAWRENCE KLEIN has been Benjamin Franklin professor
of economics at the University of Pennsylvania since
1968. He received the 1980 Nobel prize in economics for
his integration of computers and econometric models.

ROBERT LILLESTRAND is vice president and chief scientist of the Government Systems operation at Control
Data Corporation in Minneapolis, Minnesota. He developed the Columbus Research Tool in 1984.

EDWARD LORENZ, a pioneer of chaos theory, has been
a professor of meteorology at the Massachusetts Institute
of Technology since 1955.

JOSEPH RABEN is founding editor of the journal *Computers and the Humanities.*

ROBERT SHAW has a doctorate in physics and is a researcher studying dynamical systems at the University of
Illinois Center for Complex Systems Research.

BENJAMIN SHNEIDERMAN, an associate professor of
computer science at the University of Maryland, is director of the Human-Computer Interaction Laboratory.

RANDALL STERN, vice president of research, development, and engineering at Kurzweil Computer Products,
has been developing optical scanners since 1975.

RICHARD STOLARSKI is an atmospheric chemist at the
Goddard Space Flight Center in Greenbelt, Maryland.

CHING Y. SUEN, a professor of computing science at
Concordia University in Montreal, is president of the
Canadian Image Processing and Recognition Society.

MICHAEL R. WILLIAMS, a professor of computer science
at the University of Calgary in Canada, is the author of *A
History of Computing Technology.*

JAMES A. YORKE is director of the Institute for Physical
Science and Technology at the University of Maryland in
College Park, Maryland.

Extracts from the Authorized King James Version of the
Bible, the rights of which are vested in the Crown in
perpetuity within the United Kingdom, are reproduced by
permission of Eyre & Spottiswoode Publishers, Her Maj-
esty's Printers, London. Quotations from selected poems
by William Blake and introductory text from *The Norton
Anthology of English Literature,* Volume 2, copyright
1968, are reproduced by permission of W. W. Norton &
Company, Inc. Chronology of Blake's life from Victor N.
Paananen's *William Blake,* copyright 1977, is repro-
duced by permission of Twayne Publishers, a division of
G. K. Hall & Co. The picture caption for *Elohim creating
Adam* from William Vaughan's *William Blake,* copyright
1977, is reproduced by permission of Calmann & King for
Thames & Hudson. The following was also a valuable
source of quotations: S. Foster Damon, *William Blake:
His Philosophy and Symbols,* published by Houghton
Mifflin Company, 1924.

Library of Congress Cataloging in Publication Data

The Puzzle master/by the editors of Time-Life Books, Inc.
   p.   cm.—(Understanding computers)
  Bibliography: p.
  Includes index.
  1. Computers—History.   I. Time-Life Books.
II. Series.
QA76.17.P89 1988   004'.09—dc19   88-20080
                                        CIP

ISBN 0-8094-5741-5
ISBN 0-8094-5742-3 (lib. bdg.)

For information on and a full description of any of the Time-
Life Books series listed, please write:
Reader Information
Time-Life Customer Service
P.O. Box C-32068
Richmond, Virginia 23261-2068